'As much as is necessary; not as much as possible.'

'The measure of a good HACCP system is not how complicated you can make it, but how simple it can be to ensure food safety.'

## The Author

Andrew Owen-Griffiths trained as an Environmental Health Officer at Preston Borough Council and Salford University, and qualified in 1989. He has worked almost exclusively since then in food safety, both as an enforcement officer in Preston and Wakefield and as a Food Safety Consultant in the UK. He specialises in the training of food safety. He was employed for five years running the Health Development Unit of Wakefield Metropolitan District Council and also training environmental health in the Middle East.

He currently lives with his wife, Tracy and two sons Meara and Elliott, in Dublin, Ireland, where he works for the European Commission Food and Veterinary Office.

## Acknowledgments

My thanks must go to many who helped with this manual. To all the premises that have suffered my audits, and the people who have suffered my enthusiasm for HACCP on training courses. Particular thanks must be made to a few who have had particular influence in my writing of this, though they may not know it; Kay Mortimore and Carole Lister, Helen Freeman, the two Richards (North and Sprenger), all the Health Development Unit of Wakefield M.D.C, Chris Woffenden, John Barrow, Robert Easton, Colleen Rudge, and Adnan from Dubai Municipality.

My family must also be thanked; particularly Tracy for whom proofreading HACCP notes has proved the ideal cure for insomnia.

Thank you.

# HACCP*Works*

## Integrated Food Safety Management for Food Businesses

1

2

**Andrew Owen-Griffiths**

First published June 2001
2nd Edition 2002
3rd Edition 2005

## © HIGHFIELD.CO.UK LTD

"Vue Pointe", Spinney Hill, Sprotbrough,
Doncaster DN5 7LY, U.K.
**Tel: +44 (0)845 2260350**
**Facsimile: +44 (0)845 2260360**
**e-mail: jayne@highfield.co.uk**
**websites:**
**www.highfield.co.uk**
**www.foodsafetytrainers.co.uk**

ISBN 1 904544 - 36 - 3

# Contents

# Planning
## Using this Manual

Most people who are using this manual will be required to understand more than just the key concepts of HACCP, since they will be involved in its implementation or enforcement. The integration of HACCP with other management systems and the support needed are crucial to success. It is for this reason that the manual covers more than just HACCP principles, and is laid out from the planning stage, via the implementation of the key elements, to the maintaining of HACCP in practice.

The manual is therefore divided into three sections:

The **planning** stage is referenced by a

●

in the top right hand corner of the page, and covers background information and the prerequisites to HACCP.

The **implementation** stage, the core principles of Codex HACCP are similarly referenced by a

▼

and

**Maintain**, the outcomes and maintenance of HACCP, termed post-HACCP principles are referenced by

◆

Throughout the text there are practical examples from various HACCP plans. There are recap (multiple choice) questions at five stages of the manual. Particularly with HACCP teams in mind, there are short exercises in the appendices that are designed to be used at different stages of HACCP team development. A glossary ('jargon buster') and references for further information are provided in the appendices.

Whilst it would be possible to skip directly to the core principles, as many students might want to, it is recommended the text is approached from the beginning and each stage consolidated with the recap section, before progressing to the next. Without an understanding of the prerequisites, no HACCP system will work effectively.

HACCP is a changing creature that has different meanings in different situations. It must also be personalised to your process and industry sector. Thus at the end of each of the core principles, and at crucial points elsewhere, a page is left for you to personalise the manual with your own comments/parameters etc.

The author would welcome feedback from anyone reading or using this manual, and can be contacted via the publishers, Highfield Publications, whose contact details can be found on the cover.

# Foreword

Despite nearly 30 years of development, HACCP is still in a state of evolution. The efforts of the Codex Alimentarius Food Safety Committee have resulted only relatively recently in the uniform approach of seven HACCP principles, and yet even within this restraint there are numerous variations of protocol and presentation.

What is new is the uniform global acceptance of the need for HACCP, its enshrinement in legislation and the widespread need for training and information. This text has its roots in the enforcement of HACCP principles and in HACCP training, and the desire of students to have an affordable and accessible text.

*With this background, it is seen that there are four objectives for this manual:*

**1.**

To provide a text for those who are learning about HACCP, either within the food industry, on a recognised HACCP course or as students of Environmental Health, Food Science and Technology and related courses. The text should be comprehensive and accessible. It should contain realistic examples to aid understanding and be laid out to ensure easy referencing.

**2.**

To provide practical guidance to those who are implementing HACCP in their premises. In particular the members of a HACCP team.

**3.**

To provide a basis for discussion to move toward a more uniform approach to HACCP application and enforcement.

**4.**

To progress the development of the integration of HACCP with other related systems.

# Introduction

Food safety is more important now than it has ever been. The public perception of what is safe, and the associated demands this places on the food industry, can be routinely seen in the popular as well as professional press. The fines for non-compliance are escalating, and the consequences of failure are greater than they have ever been with the emergence of pathogens such as *E. coli O157*.

HACCP embodies the direction in which public health in the western world is moving. The traditional approach to any health problem has been to monitor the extent of the problem, apply scientific hypotheses as to causes (risk assessment) and then address these causes in turn (risk management). However scientific this approach, it is always reactive, only addressing existing problems that have already caused illness. Whilst these principles are valid and worth holding on to, a move toward proactive public health has shifted the emphasis. HACCP embodies such principles in being a tool that can be used to not only predict problems but to provide the vehicle for a combined and holistic attack on these potential problems. It is in this area that the application of HACCP principles often fails.

Against this background, there are mounting pressures and changes on enforcement authorities, to the extent that even if education is the most effective approach, it is used as a last resort. The responsibility for food safety lies squarely on the shoulder of the food industry, placed there by the press and by the altering attitude of both national and international bodies. HACCP is the tool presented to the food industry as the means of accepting that responsibility, in legislation or otherwise. In many industry sectors, it is the pressure from those businesses with great purchasing power, the supermarkets and large pub chains, or the desire to enter a global market, which is forcing the change.

HACCP stands for Hazard Analysis Critical Control Point. It is more than this acronym though; it epitomises the principle of proactive food hygiene, and the integration of food safety into the whole corporate ethos. To this end, therefore, it is both a principle and an ideal, and before someone says to you, 'it is only common sense,' it is applied and structured common sense.

Despite our best efforts, I do not believe HACCP will always result in zero defects in most situations; human and mechanical error, sabotage and system error are an integral part of a food industry. Let us not examine the failings of HACCP when next there is a product complaint, recall or food poisoning, but rather what improvements it has achieved and who failed in its implementation; for the missed hazards, infrequent monitoring, inadequate critical limit or incomplete corrective action are the fault of the HACCP co-ordinator, not the system itself. More often than not though the failure will be in the inadequate maintenance of the HACCP system, and this is where it becomes important that the system is developed in-house and integrated with the existing systems of the company. This is the arena that HACCP is entering and is the basis of this manual.

Never then has there been a greater need for a widespread understanding of HACCP. Slowly that need is being met as short courses are developed, and industry groups get to grips with the significance to their clients. Peer pressure helps as industry proves that it can be practically implemented, and it can work. Unfortunately, it is left to large-scale failings such as Wishaw (29) to push the case for HACCP far quicker than the government intended. Reactive again.

Despite this there is little in the way of material to help those implementing HACCP. Many training materials are neither accessible nor cheap to the medium-size producer or the caterer. There is little for those who have to enforce HACCP systems, external auditors and Environmental Health Officers. This manual is designed to meet that need.

# The History of HACCP

Given that many people approach HACCP as a new concept and 'newfangled idea', it is often a surprise to them to learn that the basis of a modern HACCP system lies with the NASA space programme way back in the early 1960s.

Prior to the inception of the HACCP programme there was very much a dependency in the food industry on good practice models and end-product testing. The inadequacy of rapid microbiological testing procedures in the present day, let alone early 1960, means that product safety dependent on end-product sampling is very hit and miss. Thus, concepts of quality control and zero defect sampling had to be disregarded.

The NASA programme had various problems with food production for consumption in zero gravity; including concern over microbiological safety. Whilst some concerns, such as the size of food particles and floating crumbs which could have led to short circuits, were addressable by existing technology, it was microbiological safety that posed problems. The development of a system of safe food production was undertaken with the Pillsbury Corporation, and it was this company that went on to develop the system for more widespread application. In 1971, a more refined version was presented at the United States International Conference on Food Safety. It described the three key principles that became the precursor of the seven point codex HACCP we use today: identification of hazards; identification of critical control points; and the monitoring of these points. Reaction to a large botulism outbreak in canned soup in the USA (1972) led to these principles becoming the basis of law to legislate the canning of low-acid foods. The model started to become universally accepted, and became enshrined in legislation.

The first step toward widespread use of HACCP in the UK came with the Food Safety Act 1990. The defence of 'Due Diligence', and the responsibility for food safety being placed upon the proprietor made the HACCP concept attractive and soon commercially necessary.

With the free movement of goods within the European Economic Area, and an increase in external markets, the requirement for a guaranteed uniform means of assuring safety at the point of production made HACCP very tempting. The World Trade Organisation certainly found it so. In 1991, the World Health Organisation's 'Codex Alimentarius' organisation for the establishment of world food standards published a report entitled 'Guidelines for the Application of the Hazard Analysis and Critical Control Point System' (7). This is probably the second step that promoted HACCP's international recognition, and the most important for the UK.

It did not take long for the European Commission to adopt the HACCP principles, as established by Codex. In 1993 Directive 93/43/EEC (10) imposed some HACCP principles on all member states, although stopping short of including verification and documentation stages. And so in 1995 the UK Food Safety (General Food Hygiene) Regulations, Regulation 4 (3) (20) came to fruition, although enforcement, application and understanding would take a little bit longer.

# The History of HACCP

During the same period, HACCP was included in a range of product specific (vertical) legislation in both the European Union and in the USA. Its inclusion in three UK vertical regulations, and in shellfish regulations in the USA, set the ground for lots of development of HACCP in primary production; particularly in the USA for beef and pork production. It has to be said, however, that the legislative wording and implementation was variable and is still developing, with the requirement for HACCP absent in Europe for raw processing of animal products. It also became a necessary industry sector document, with every federation producing documents or seminar papers that applied HACCP to their industry. A number of companies and governments also tried to shift the previous emphasis of HACCP on production/ manufacturing to more general catering processes. The production of systems for the National Health Service in the UK, the Assured Safe Catering (ASC) System *(11)* from the British Department of Health and the inclusion of HACCP in the USA 'food code' adequately illustrate this movement.

The failure of the UK food industry to fully adopt HACCP principles, and the failure of enforcement officers to enforce it, are by now well advertised by 21 deaths from *E.coli O157*, and the subsequent Pennington report *(29)*. The strong recommendation in this report that HACCP be enforced led to a change of tune from the Department of Health and accelerated the learning process for large numbers of enforcement officers and the meat industry. An 'Accelerated HACCP training programme' *(26)* for meat managers funded by the Department of Health and administered by the Meat and Livestock Commission in 1998/9 was mirrored by a similar 'Accredited HACCP Course' in the USA (administered by the National Meat Association) as the HACCP requirement for small meat and poultry premises came into force in late January 1999. The requirement for documented HACCP principles in butchers' shops selling raw and cooked products in the UK was soon to follow.

From either an industry or enforcement perspective the importance of HACCP is set to increase, both in the UK and globally (see Legislation section). From an industry perspective, the requirement for HACCP as part of a requirement for national and global food movement will be just as important as the increased strength of HACCP in both legislation and its enforcement.

We have come a long way, but probably have just as far to go.

# The Advantages and Disadvantages of HACCP

## Advantages

A logical starting point to introducing or enforcing HACCP is the understanding of the need for it beyond any legislative requirement. Sometimes, desire for change will be met by inertia. We must believe in the benefits and be able to relay them articulately to others. Many of these benefits can be made company specific and thus all the more powerful as tools to promote the need for investment in HACCP.

### To illustrate legal compliance

Beyond illustrating any legal provision for HACCP/self-regulation the documentation inherent in a HACCP system serves well to illustrate legal compliance, with, for example, temperature control requirements. This serves to facilitate easier liaison with enforcing bodies, but also helps in forming the basis of assuring legal product compliance for the companies that purchase the product.

### To ensure safety

HACCP is safety centred, and thus provides a focus for the company on safety. It is also proactive rather than reactive and can be cost-effective when compared, particularly, to microbiological end-product testing.

Within any company there will be a host of practices and procedures, written or otherwise. Many of these will contribute to safety, or to quality or just be good practice. HACCP enables a focus to be made on safety; creating a bridge between a multitude of untargeted practices and those that must be done for safety. This then allows monitoring to be carried out just at these points to ensure product safety.

### To facilitate institutional changes

The introduction of HACCP into a company can be a significant step, and can therefore be an ideal opportunity to introduce structural or institutional change or to set up new procedures that would be difficult to establish alone. This comment can be particularly pertinent with daily monitoring that often meets resistance; HACCP provides clear instruction and the explanation of why the monitoring is necessary. It is also useful to revisit the allocation of responsibility for hygiene at all levels when introducing HACCP.

The completion of improvements as part of the development of prerequisite programmes also offers a valuable opportunity to create improvements that would otherwise be difficult to justify.

### To provide markers to measure change

If carried out properly HACCP will be preceded by a monitorable baseline audit. This and the recording and monitoring inherent in the system mean that improvements in performance can be monitored and demonstrated at board level. This may well be essential to illustrate the cost-benefit of the process.

### To provide a framework for quality changes

Whilst targeted initially on safety issues the framework of HACCP can be just as effective at controlling quality issues. All that is required is alteration to the assessment of significance in hazards, alteration of the scope and tuning of targets and critical limits. If this is done, however, to work efficiently it is essential that there is a clear delineation between safety and quality.

### As a marketing tool

Awareness of food safety in general, and HACCP in particular, is increasing within the industry and the public. It is usual for a purchaser of products to require written confirmation of a supplier's HACCP system

# The Advantages and Disadvantages of HACCP

## Complacency

Once the system is established two areas of concern can arise. First, overconfidence in the system can mean that good practice outside the CCPs is neglected, and second, there is not constant verification and review to ensure that the system works properly and is representative of what actually happens in food production. Good management and regular reviews by the HACCP team are essential.

## Microbiological based

The history of HACCP in the control of microbiological hazards means that most books and training materials concentrate on this area. The reality is that many, if not most, manufacturers are concerned predominately about physical and chemical contaminants. If this is the case, a lot of confusion can be generated in the assessment of significance of hazards and of CCPs.

## Global variations

Pressure from international bodies has created a rapid expansion of HACCP in many countries and cultures. This does not mean, however, that HACCP is always going to be uniformly applied. Differences exist, for example, across the Atlantic, where CCPs tend to be imposed, or in Third World countries where HACCP does not have a sufficient good practice base to be effective.

Consideration of the above issues at an early stage can normally limit their negative effect.

# Legislative Framework

The following summary of the legislative provisions that relate to HACCP is made on the basis of UK statutes. As the majority of the legislation is an enactment of European directives, the general legislative provision, but not exact wording, can be used for the 15 member states of the European Community. Anyone carrying out enforcement action should refer to the current copy of the legislation referred to for exact wording.

Even before the first mention of HACCP in legislation there is a number of areas of the law that contribute to HACCP and create a framework for later specific requirements in law. Most of these are contained in the **Food Safety Act 1990** *(15)* and related Codes of Practice. The first of these is the statutory defence of **'due diligence' (section 21 (1))**.

**'...In any proceedings for an offence under any of the preceding provisions... it shall...be a defence for the person charged to prove that he took all reasonable precautions and exercised all due diligence to avoid the commission of the offence.'**

Based on previous case law in which it was held that an offence was prosecutable even if it was unavoidable (Smedley v Breed), due diligence is the first introduction in food production of the idea of companies doing all that is possible. It is the first large step towards stating that responsibility for food safety lies with the proprietor and not the enforcement authority and therefore is a precursor to the proactive principles of HACCP. As it is usually only demonstrable in a court by documentation, the formalised, accurate documentation of a HACCP system will contribute towards the likely success of such a defence. In most situations, however, greater benefit is seen in a visible HACCP system demonstrating to an enforcement officer the likelihood of a due diligence defence; in which case the officer should not proceed with the prosecution.

The above provision relating to prosecution was described under the original Code of Practice No. 9 'Food Safety Inspections' *(16)* issued under the Food Safety Act. It contained other areas that relate to HACCP; the nature of the enforcement inspection being based upon the principle of hazard analysis and that priority should be given to inspecting the hazard analysis system within the company. A summary of the pertinent sections is provided below.

**Section 24**
**Inspections should:**

- **include a preliminary assessment of the food safety hazards associated with the business and**

- **look at whether a business has a satisfactory system (a 'hazard analysis system') for assessing food hazards...the approach to inspections should be changed significantly where there is such a system in place.**

This part serves to illustrate the legal standing given to HACCP principles as a keystone of food law enforcement. The code of practice proceeded to look at the enforcement of Regulation 4 (3) of the Food Safety (General Food Hygiene) Regulations 1995 *(20)*.

**Section 61**
**In certain high-risk businesses and operations a formal documented hazard analysis system based on specialist advice may be necessary to establish effective control.**

This can be seen as indicative of the direction of food law beyond the current legal minimum in horizontal legislation to a stage where documentation is required.

# Legislative Framework

Food legislation is divided into two types: horizontal and vertical, as shown in the following diagram:

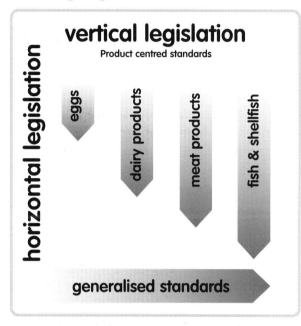

## Horizontal legislation

UK food law is strongly governed by the requirements of the European Union. Most specifically, the **European Directive 93/43/EEC** (1993) *(10)* acts upon the recommendations of the Codex Alimentarius to move us towards a legal requirement for HACCP. This general requirement for all products (horizontal legislation) was followed by a number of directives that posed a more stringent requirement for HACCP principles, including documentation specific to certain products under certain conditions. Most, however, still fell short of requiring all of the seven CODEX HACCP principles. The requirement of these vertical directives is dealt with later. The horizontal legislation falls short of HACCP as a legal requirement, enabling the development of 'HACCP-type systems' related to catering in particular that can still meet the desired end point of safe food but without following all the protocols of a formal HACCP system. The direct terminology in the legislation is for 'self-regulation' following the principles of HACCP as listed (five principles only). The

debate over what constitutes legal compliance and how this differs from HACCP is debated under Section 6 of this manual 'Types of HACCP'.

The horizontal requirement has been embodied in UK legislation in the **Food Safety (General Food Hygiene) Regulations 1995** *(20)*, where Regulation 4 (3) has been a legal requirement since September 1995. The wording of the requirement is similar to the wording within the European Directive, and hence this has not been duplicated. A summary of this requirement is offered below.

### Regulation 4 (3)

**A proprietor of a food business shall identify any step in the activities of the food business which is critical to ensuring food safety and ensure that adequate safety procedures are identified, implemented, maintained and reviewed on the basis of the following principles:**

**A. Analysis of the potential food hazards in a food business operation;**

**B. Identification of the points in those operations where food hazards may occur;**

**C. Deciding which of the points identified are critical to ensuring food safety ('critical points')**

**D. Identification and implementation of effective control and monitoring procedures at these critical points; and**

**E. Review of the analysis of food hazards, the critical points and the control and monitoring procedures periodically, and whenever the food business' operations change.**

Whilst this is an important legislative

provision it is one that is very difficult to enforce. In essence, if a proprietor has a basic understanding of the hazards inherent in the given operation, is implementing necessary controls and monitoring, and is able to articulate this to an officer, enforcement is unlikely. Without a requirement for documentation, evidence is normally from a dramatic failure that illustrates lack of control; food poisoning or a prosecution for numerous other offences. In such an instance the addition of the extra offence rarely has a significant effect on the overall fine. The number of Improve-ment Notices for non-compliance with this section is, however, on the increase, and a documented HACCP system (even one with failings) may help in preventing such action.

The staggered enforcement of the legal requirement (under Department of Health Guidance) meant that the first legal actions really only began in 1997, and then slowly. Without the adverse publicity offered by the Pennington Report (29) and the Wishaw E. coli O157 outbreak, it would have been even slower. This 'lead-in period' was designed to give time for both enforcers and industry to grasp the implications of the legal requirement. It is probably fair to say that there was a learning curve also for the magistrates, for whom visual and emotive offences are much more comprehensible.

The advent of the **'Industry Guides to Good Practice'** (2) has done much to enhance understanding of the legal requirement to each industry sector, and the practical and understandable layout must be commended. It is useful to repeat two lines from the Catering Guide regarding the legal status of documentation:

*'In some cases it may be useful to keep records.'*
*'This regulation (Regulation 4 (3)) does not demand fully documented "classic" HACCP but caterers should bear in mind that a brief written explanation...would be helpful in showing the Environmental Health Officer*

*(EHO) that this regulation has been complied with.'*

Even into the 21st century the food industry is slow to grasp the significance of the legal requirement. This situation is exacerbated by variances in terminology ('HACCP' or 'risk assessment' to mean the legal requirement for 'self-regulation'), variances in levels of education (both geographically and by industry sector), by language barriers and by great variations of the interpretation of the legal requirement. ('There must be a written HACCP', 'you must keep fridge temperature records', 'the HACCP must legally be product specific', etc.) A concerted education programme, uniformly applied with agreed objectives and terminology might have been successful, but has been sadly lacking. Even 'official' promotional materials changed style and terminology throughout the educational period (the period before increased priority for enforcement). The only area that comes close is the Department of Health-funded MLC 'Accelerated HACCP Project' (26), designed to provide the proprietors of retail butcher's premises with the materials and training to be able to implement a 'workable HACCP system' prior to it becoming a legal requirement as part of the licensing of butcher's premises. An effort that must be commended.

**The Food Safety (General Food Hygiene) (Butchers' Shops) Amendment Regulations 2000** (23), which came in force in May 2000 provides a requirement for a documented HACCP. Commendably, the associated guidance details the emphasis on 'practicable and manageable arrangements' and on the grouping of food items for the purpose of analysis. Following the recommendations of the Pennington enquiry the requirement for documentation in all high-risk premises is inevitable. If this is not unilaterally done by the UK the requirement will be forced by the European

# Legislative Framework

Commission review of food law, and a new food safety regulation.

## Vertical legislation

The requirements in vertical legislation are generally closer to all of the HACCP principles, including the requirement for documentation. The problem here is the variation in the requirements and in the wording given. In the case of the raw product related regulations (for example, **The Fresh Meat (Hygiene and Inspection) Regulations 1995** *(17)* and **The Wild Game Meat (Hygiene and Inspection) Regulations 1995** *(18)*, there is no requirement, as yet, for HACCP. Instead, there is a variety of schedules that impose standards and in some instances an imposed sampling regime. This is in sharp contrast to the USA where requirements for HACCP in the production of pork and beef were one of the first legislative requirements.

This does really necessitate an examination of the wording in each regulation to illustrate the variation. All wording comes from the relevant UK legislation and not the associated directive. For enforcement purposes, full reference should be made to the relevant regulation and any amendments.

The first vertical provision to refer to HACCP principles was **The Meat Products (Hygiene) Regulations 1994** *(14,)* which came into force on 1 January 1995. The development of HACCP in legislation can be illustrated by comparison of the wording in these regulations with the provision in later regulations **(The Food Safety (Fishery Products and Live Shellfish) Regulations 1998** *(21)*, for example). Much is made at each step of the provision being 'acceptable to the enforcement authority', a somewhat obvious and unhelpful statement that is thankfully omitted in later vertical provisions. The wording falls far short of a requirement for HACCP, but a requirement

for the identification of critical points, monitoring and documentation is evident, embodying the key principles from which HACCP originated. The Regulations apply to all premises where meat products are produced for wholesale. This does not include retail sale or any other sale direct to caterers (exempting much small-scale production by retail butchers). Any premises to which the Regulations are applicable must receive prior and annual approval and meet a number of schedules of standards (not all are applicable to every premises). It is my experience, however, that a significant proportion have not sought, or been given, the required approval. These provide a more stringent standard than the horizontal regulations, including the regulation applicable to HACCP principles, which comes under Part 4: Requirements Applicable to all Food Premises.

**Regulation 13-1**
**The occupier of an establishment shall take all necessary measures to ensure that, at all stages of production or rewrapping of meat products and other products of animal origin, these Regulations are complied with and shall carry out his own checks to ensure:**

A) **That critical points in the establishment relative to the process used are identified and acceptable to the enforcement authority; and**

B) **That methods for monitoring and controlling such critical points are established and acceptable to the enforcement authority; and**

D) **That as far as is reasonable and practicable a record in permanent form is kept and made available to the enforcement authority...and is kept for a period of at least two years... Or six months after the minimum**

**durability if it cannot be stored at ambient.**

Following on, Section G is linked in that it has a requirement for the ability to withdraw products in the event of an imminent health risk. The unstated requirement is therefore for product traceability and a product recall procedure. For most meat products premises the above is interpreted as requiring a written HACCP-type system, and in many situations a classic HACCP approach is the most logical as products are well defined and have little variation.

There is little change in **The Dairy Products (Hygiene) Regulations 1995** *(22)*. Wording regarding the identification of critical points, monitoring and testing remains virtually the same; only the phrase 'acceptable to the enforcement authority' has been removed. The nature of the defined product does mean that the Regulations are more prescriptive, in both the nature and frequency of sampling regimes, and in the critical limits for thermal processing set under separate schedules.

The requirement for hazard analysis is found in a section (Part 6) that is applicable to all dairy establishments.

## Duties of occupier or purchaser of raw milk for sale

**Regulation 13-(1) ...the occupier of a dairy establishment shall:**

**B) Carry out their own checks to ensure:**
1. **That critical points in the dairy establishment relative to the processes used there are identified;**
2. **That methods for monitoring and controlling such critical points are established;**
3. **That appropriate tests are carried out to detect any residues...**

**C) That as so far as is reasonable and**

**practicable a record in permanent form is kept in respect of the matters specified in subparagraph (B) above:**
1. **...in the case of products that cannot be stored under ambient conditions... For a period of not less than two months from the end of the minimum durability indication... and**
2. **in the case of any other dairy product, for a period of not less than two years;**

**H) Provision for traceability and withdrawal procedures if necessary.**

As earlier this is seen as a requirement for a written hazard analysis, the requirement for two years records of monitoring and for traceability requiring a significant amount of documentation. The small number of products normally involved, the simple thermal process and the defined critical limits and test parameters make this a relatively easy task to undertake.

The final vertical requirement for HACCP is in the much more recent **Food Safety (Fishery Products and Live Shellfish) Regulations 1998** *(21)*. The change in wording moves the legal requirement closer to a full requirement for HACCP, and is comparable to a similar legal requirement in the USA. The debate over safety definitions is tempered by the use of the phrase 'safe and hygienic production'.

## Obligations upon food business proprietors operating factory vessels and establishments

**Regulation 28-(4) A food business proprietor who is operating a factory vessel or approved fishery products establishment shall carry out checks at his establishment based on the following principles:**

# Legislative Framework

A. Identification of points critical to ensuring safe and hygienic production in his vessel or establishment on the basis of the manufacturing process used, and for these purposes a critical point is any point, step or procedure at which control can be applied and a food safety hazard be prevented, eliminated or reduced to acceptable levels;

B. Establishment and implementation of methods for monitoring and checking such critical points;

C. Taking samples for analysis...

D. Keeping a written record or a record registered in an indelible fashion of the preceding points (for at least two years).

At present, there is no specific requirement for HACCP principles in UK vertical legislation for meat products (in sharp contrast to the USA). The debate over criticality in relation to primary processing of meat is ongoing in the European Union. At the current time **The Fresh Meat (Hygiene and Inspection) Regulations 1995, Wild Game Meat (Hygiene and Inspection) Regulations 1995** and **Poultry Meat, Farmed Game Bird Meat and Rabbit Meat (Hygiene and Inspection) Regulations 1995** centre very much on the control exerted by veterinary inspection in enforcing various schedules, rather than placing responsibility on the proprietor.

## The future direction

Whilst the exact future of HACCP within UK legislation is unknown, the direction in which it is moving is not in doubt. As with the USA, the general requirement for the application of HACCP principles will expand, and more and more products will be targeted by a specific requirement, often with associated imposed parameters. Throughout the European Community, the enforcement of existing requirements will be raised as the European Commission plays a greater role in the inspection of member states enforcement.

The current horizontal requirement in all premises for the current five steps will therefore gradually become more strictly enforced. Stage by stage the requirement for documentation will be introduced. Initially this will be premises specific (as seen in butcher's shops). This rather illogical (from a risk perspective) unilateral approach will give way to a general requirement for documentation; either through a requirement for licensing all high-risk premises, or from the issuing of a new European food regulation. It remains to be seen which will arrive first, but the effect will be the same. Perhaps the biggest unanswered question is how well the legal requirement will be introduced and enforced or educated. It is hoped some lessons will have been learnt from the failure of the implementation of the current Regulation 4 (3).

As for the vertical requirements, the variation in wording between different types of products will inevitably be removed. It is also likely that these requirements will become applicable to primary production as the European Commission, and many parallel legislative agencies, progress towards a goal of inclusive 'plough to plate' food safety.

# Types of HACCP

Inevitably, there are as many types of HACCP documents as there are food premises. Each is applied and presented slightly differently, and none can be seen to be the ideal. We can, however, group the variety of HACCPs into three: the traditional HACCP approach which is **product specific;** the more modern approach which is **process led;** and the loose application of some HACCP principles which is discussed in the section, Self-regulation: 'HACCP type systems'. The latter will include some systems developed to meet the requirements of the horizontal regulation conditions (for example, Assured Safe Catering *(11)*), and at this point comparison will be made to directly compare the legal horizontal requirements and HACCP.

## Product specific HACCP

The history of HACCP, including the Codex HACCP principles, is centred on the large-scale production of a relatively small number of products (for example, low-acid canning processes). In such a situation it is possible (and often necessary) to examine each individual product and to produce flow diagrams and HACCP plans for each. Due to the product flow diagram starting with the receipt of raw ingredients and ending with product dispatch, this type of HACCP is sometimes referred to as 'linear HACCP'.

The advantage of this is that hazards inherent in a specific ingredient in only one product will be identified, and parameters in processing that are specific to one particular product are easily highlighted. In most situations, however, detailing a whole plan for each particular product will result in excessive paperwork and so many plans that the system becomes unworkable and thus unsafe. It is usual that many products are produced that are very similar (for example, pies in a pie factory, sandwiches to the specifications of different clients, beers in a brewery) and if a product specific HACCP is followed, there will be a large number of very similar plans exhibiting the same hazards and controls. Using these will be laborious and staff intensive, and rightly be difficult to impose on a work force.

Despite the undeniable validity of product specific HACCP, historically there is very much a move, particularly in mainland Europe, toward the examination not of every product, but of every comparable process. Unless the company concerned produces a low range of products to high levels, and these all have specific hazards, it is recommended that consideration be given in the first instance to applying process led HACCP.

## Process led HACCP

Within most companies it is possible to examine the activities used in product manufacture and group them. These groups of similar processes can be dealt with as separate HACCP plans, irrespective of the product that results. For this reason some types of process led HACCP have been referred to as 'Modular HACCP'. The current direction of HACCP development is likely to mean this will become the norm rather than the exception.

The advantages from the point of resource management, understanding and targeting of critical points is obvious. The disadvantages are that it is often difficult to be clear how different processes interrelate, and thus omit an important stage. It must be clear how a product goes from one process to another, and at which point one process starts and another finishes. Any hazards that are unusual in a list of ingredients or in one particular product must also be highlighted and addressed.

The use of process led HACCP is particularly valid in relation to large-scale, catering-style operations. Similar processes are used (refrigerated storage, vegetable preparation, frying, cooling, etc.), but with varying ingredients and variations in the end product (due to seasonal ingredient changes or due to customer demand) a product specific HACCP is not possible.

This type of approach requires good

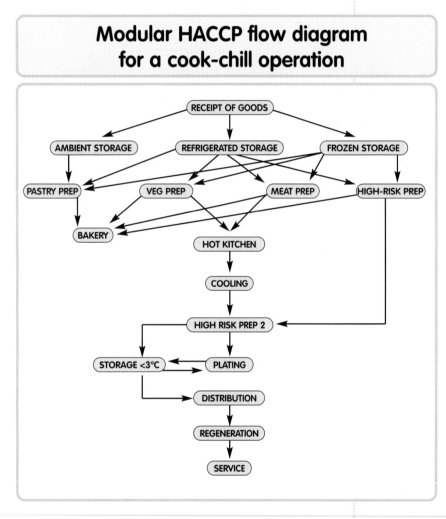

**Modular HACCP flow diagram for a cook-chill operation**

RECEIPT OF GOODS

AMBIENT STORAGE — REFRIGERATED STORAGE — FROZEN STORAGE

PASTRY PREP — VEG PREP — MEAT PREP — HIGH-RISK PREP

BAKERY

HOT KITCHEN

COOLING

HIGH RISK PREP 2

STORAGE <3°C — PLATING

DISTRIBUTION

REGENERATION

SERVICE

management to work effectively and constant review.

## Self-regulation: 'HACCP type systems'

This heading is used to describe a variety of generic approaches to impose some of the principles of HACCP on premises, usually the five principles of the horizontal legislation requirement. As this approach is normally to meet this legal requirement, the terminology (self-regulation, in-house control, etc.) is based on the legislative wording. In the UK the application of the five principles is often termed simply 'hazard

analysis'. The plan may be produced for a particular sector of the food industry or a particular company. The plan will be a framework of processes, and will normally lack any product detail. This type of approach will generally only work when the process concerned is very simple and difficult to vary from day to day (for example, preparation of a crab) or when a company by means of exactly compatible premises and processes can produce a generic flow (for example, some fast food take-away operations).

The inherent problems with such an approach are that the system will often lack detail and will not take into account product variations due to different premises, staff or regional differences. Staff have no ownership of the document and thus it is unlikely to become fully integrated into daily work practices, thus proving ineffective.

Generic HACCP can be of some use if the original document is clearly seen as a framework on which a new HACCP plan must be built. All flows must be verified and any hazards that are specific to the premises identified. Prerequisite programmes must also be confirmed at each premises. This must be clear and must be carefully managed.

The above problems with a generic HACCP can be levelled at the use of Assured Safe Catering, an attempt by the Department of Health to apply HACCP principles embodied in the Food Safety (General Food Hygiene) Regulations 1995 to caterers. It provides a list of generic hazards and controls throughout a catering operation and would serve as a good basis for undertaking hazard analysis. However, it is ineffective alone in most catering operations as it fails to address hazards specific to a particular operation, ingredient or premises. It is generally accepted as a good attempt to provide a step towards an effective system, and the following shows how such an approach can be applied to a take-away catering establishment.

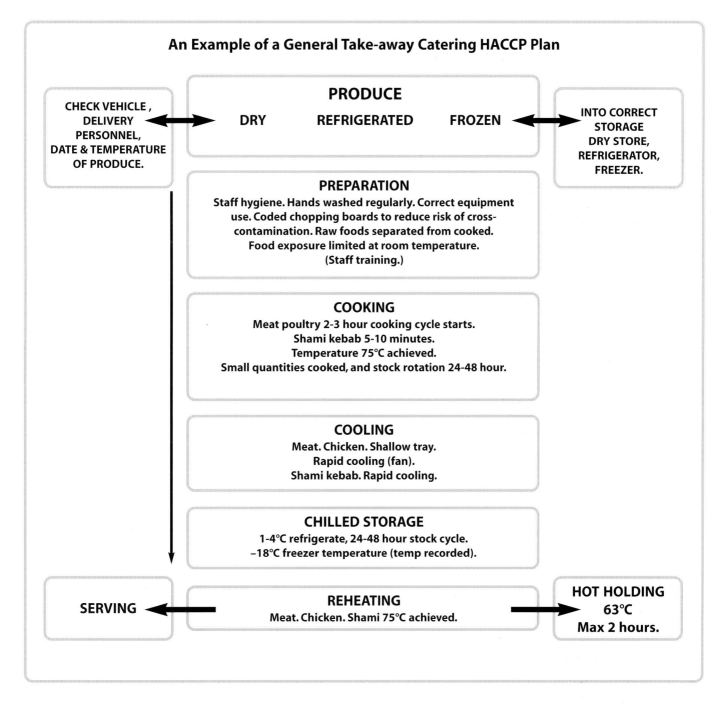

**An Example of a General Take-away Catering HACCP Plan**

**CHECK VEHICLE , DELIVERY PERSONNEL, DATE & TEMPERATURE OF PRODUCE.**

**PRODUCE**

DRY    REFRIGERATED    FROZEN

**INTO CORRECT STORAGE DRY STORE, REFRIGERATOR, FREEZER.**

**PREPARATION**
Staff hygiene. Hands washed regularly. Correct equipment use. Coded chopping boards to reduce risk of cross-contamination. Raw foods separated from cooked. Food exposure limited at room temperature. (Staff training.)

**COOKING**
Meat poultry 2-3 hour cooking cycle starts.
Shami kebab 5-10 minutes.
Temperature 75°C achieved.
Small quantities cooked, and stock rotation 24-48 hour.

**COOLING**
Meat. Chicken. Shallow tray.
Rapid cooling (fan).
Shami kebab. Rapid cooling.

**CHILLED STORAGE**
1-4°C refrigerate, 24-48 hour stock cycle.
–18°C freezer temperature (temp recorded).

**SERVING**

**REHEATING**
Meat. Chicken. Shami 75°C achieved.

**HOT HOLDING 63°C Max 2 hours.**

At this point, it is probably worth fully exploring the difference between HACCP (seven principles) and the legal requirement for self-regulation (five principles). It must be remembered that in some situations HACCP (process led or product specific) may be the best means of illustrating the legal compliance, and that ultimate interpretation of the law will be made by the courts. The following table is meant to compare and contrast the two, and should be used with reference to the wording in legislation highlighted in the section 'Legislative framework', *page 13*.

# Types of HACCP

| HACCP (Codex based) | 'Self-regulation' (Reg 4 (3)) based |
|---|---|
| 1. Not a legal requirement<br>2. Normally product or process defined<br>3. Favours large scale production of a small number of defined products | 1. A legal requirement<br>2. Normally generic<br>3. Favours small scale production of a large range of products (e.g. catering) |
| 4. Led by a 'HACCP team' | 4. Often undertaken by an individual, the terminology of the 'HACCP team' is thus inappropriate |
| 5. Supported by complex process flow diagrams | 5. Need have no flow diagrams, or can employ simple linear process step diagrams |
| 6. 'Critical control points' identified normally by the use of a 'decision tree' | 6. 'Which points are critical' are less exposed to scientific scrutiny. Decision trees rarely used |
| 7. Effective control and monitoring requires strict written procedures. Targets/tolerances and/or critical limits are exact, easily monitored and variable from product to product | 7. Monitoring requirements are less stringent and normally good catering practice. 'Critical limits' are normally those set by legislation and rarely vary. Parameters are often difficult to monitor against |
| 8. Corrective action procedures are documented | 8. Corrective action is not stated as a legal requirement and need not be documented, but is part of 'effective control' |
| 9. Supported by extensive documentation | 9. Need have no documentation legally, or if documented a summary can suffice |
| 10. Normally supported by sampling regimes as part of verification | 10. No legal requirement for verification/validation |
| 11. Rigid | 11. Flexible |

An understanding of the difference of approach is important from both an enforcement and education perspective. All too often, owners/proprietors of premises are told to implement HACCP without full understanding of what they are being told to do. In some instances, confusion arises with Health and Safety Risk Assessment, for example, relatively low-risk catering premises have been asked to produce flow diagrams and HACCP plans for every menu item. In other cases, debate over critical control points and the use of protocols such as the decision tree are enough to confuse most people.

From an educational perspective, it is imperative that the terminology is clear in the mind of the educator, and that professionals consistently use the same terminology. The decision as to the type and extent of the HACCP also forms an important part of principle one of Codex HACCP and thus needs to be understood by all involved.

# Where do I start ?

HACCP can be considered the vehicle that allows a journey of change. The important first questions to be asked of anyone proposing a HACCP system are 'where do we hope to arrive?' and 'from what point are we starting?'. If we are able to make this clear, the journey is likely to be a lot smoother. In other words, it is sometimes wise to sacrifice a swift journey to an incorrect destination to allow a slower but smoother ride to the correct one.

The obvious starting point for any company is where it is at present. The problem is that many companies are somewhat unsure as to where that is in relation to food safety, or they have staff members with differing perceptions. The inherent tendency is to look ahead and set off at a run. This can create untold havoc with the safe running of a HACCP system, as existing systems serve as the foundation on which the HACCP programme is built. The supporting systems are dealt with in the next section as 'prerequisites' to a HACCP system; although not part of the key principles of Codex HACCP they are the pillars on which HACCP is built and must be integrated, the parallel management systems must be made to converge and interlink. In training, I use the illustration of all the tangled wires that run from the back of a computer. They all serve different individual purposes (as do the many systems found in a food business), but they have a joint overall aim, the efficient running of my computer (as HACCP and other systems have the aim of food safety). What HACCP allows us to do is tidy up and bind these wires together so that they run parallel and interlinked. They are then focused and controllable. This principle can be termed **'parallel systems integration,'** and is a form of 'joined up food safety thinking' sadly lacking in many food safety systems.

The evaluation of existing procedures at this stage, particularly generalised practices such as structure, pest control, etc. (termed 'Good Hygiene Practices' or GHP) will also help when hazard analysis is being undertaken in 'working out' of the process non-specific hazards (see principle one). This again is a common failing of many HACCP systems because it is not explicitly outlined in CODEX and thus in many training or reference materials.

The assessment of the current status of food safety, the starting point in the above analogy, should be recorded in some way; this is sometimes termed a **baseline audit**, and is in effect a snapshot of the premises prior to HACCP implementation.

This should be strongly considered for the following reasons:

- There is less chance of omitting, or duplicating, an existing system.
- It enables long-term monitoring of improvements to illustrate the savings or improvements the HACCP system has created.
- GHP is effectively assessed to allow adequate assessment of hazards at principle one.
- The incorporating and linking to existing systems sometimes makes the 'selling' of HACCP easier to existing staff.

It is likely, but not necessarily always the case that the people who will carry out the baseline audit will be the people who will proceed to form the HACCP team. In doing the audit, there is a multitude of existing procedures and documentation that requires consideration. The following list is a summary and detail is provided in the prerequisites section as mentioned. A company will have numerous industry and company specific policies and standards that require consideration that the baseline audit must embrace.

# Where do I start ?

| | |
|---|---|
| Quality management procedures | **(See section 'HACCP and ISO quality management)** |
| Food Safety Policy<br>Statement of Intent<br>Responsibilities<br>Standards<br>    Ingredient lists/specifications<br>    Menus<br>    Product specifications<br>    Client specifications<br>    Legislation<br>    Industry guides/Codes of Practice | **(See section 'HACCP and the management of safety)** |
| Training standards | **(See HACCP and training)** |
| Good manufacturing practice/good catering<br>    practice<br>Cleaning schedules<br>Glass/metal/wood policies<br>Visitors procedures<br>Personal hygiene and training programmes<br>Maintenance schedules<br>Pest control<br>Waste management<br>Monitoring procedures | **(See examples of GMP)** |
| Complaints procedures and levels | **(See 'Some post-HACCP principles')** |
| Sampling regimes and standards | |
| Crisis management | |

Whilst integration is crucial, it is worth sounding a word of caution. The integration must be HACCP led, and must not involve slotting HACCP into, and thus maintaining, existing systems automatically. The worst approach would be to start with existing monitoring and work backwards on the assumption these are the CCPs. This is unfortunately a situation that becomes evident in the auditing of many HACCP systems.

Having considered resourcing and the existing status of food safety systems within the company, the next question to consider is where the journey will end, that is, where do you want to go? and how the success of the journey will be assessed.

The exact details will need establishing by the HACCP team, but it is necessary at this stage to give them some parameters within which to work. The most important of these will be a rough timescale; whether a process or product led HACCP is required; how they will report to the sponsor or board; any required protocols on HACCP or how it is to be presented and how the system will be launched.

Another important consideration at this stage is of resourcing. This can be in forms of money, staff, other resources (including administrative support) or knowledge. All too often a person is told as part of their existing role to create a HACCP system. It may as well be added, 'but do it as quickly as possible and ensure nothing changes', and this can be one of the more frustrating realities for food safety professionals.

## Implementing the system/system management

There are a number of project management systems, computer based or otherwise, that can be used for the implementation of a HACCP plan. Different managers will have their existing favourites and protocols and it is not the remit of this manual to impose management styles. For those unfamiliar with these systems, or those who decide they are unnecessary, the following basic principles must be considered:

1. Clearly defined objectives should be established, which can then be monitored.
2. Project resourcing should be clear.
3. Overall timescale and proposed timescale for meeting specific objectives. (Termed 'milestones' in this manual.)
4. Reporting criteria.
5. Responsibilities.

One of the objectives should be that each step of HACCP should consider the integration of other systems. This in effect will create a gradual convergence of what are currently parallel systems. It is not suggested these should meet to become one document; this would be huge and unworkable. However, the systems should be integrated by cross-referencing and not duplicated.

One way of managing the improvement of a system from one point (point A) to another (point B) is by a **gap analysis.** Whilst the exact layout will vary, this is essentially the identification of necessary improvements, their allocation to staff members with a strict time scale and their 'writing off' on completion. It also therefore creates a record of the improvement made.

Gap analyses will be useful at many stages of HACCP implementation, and during the review of HACCP. Whilst the principles are that of any project management, the gap analysis is at its best in the management of small-scale improvements, not in the whole project. It is however a useful tool to learn at this stage.

When examining these principles, one underlying idea is that review and assessment should occur formally at a number of steps within the process. The following diagram is designed to graphically show the logical progression of the stages already discussed, and creates a useful framework for the setting of review. It is up to the individual to consider the timescale, as it will depend on the size and complexity of the company. This is a simplified and informal diagram, formal ones can be produced by computer packages such as Project Manager Pro or Microsoft Manager.

# HACCP implementation

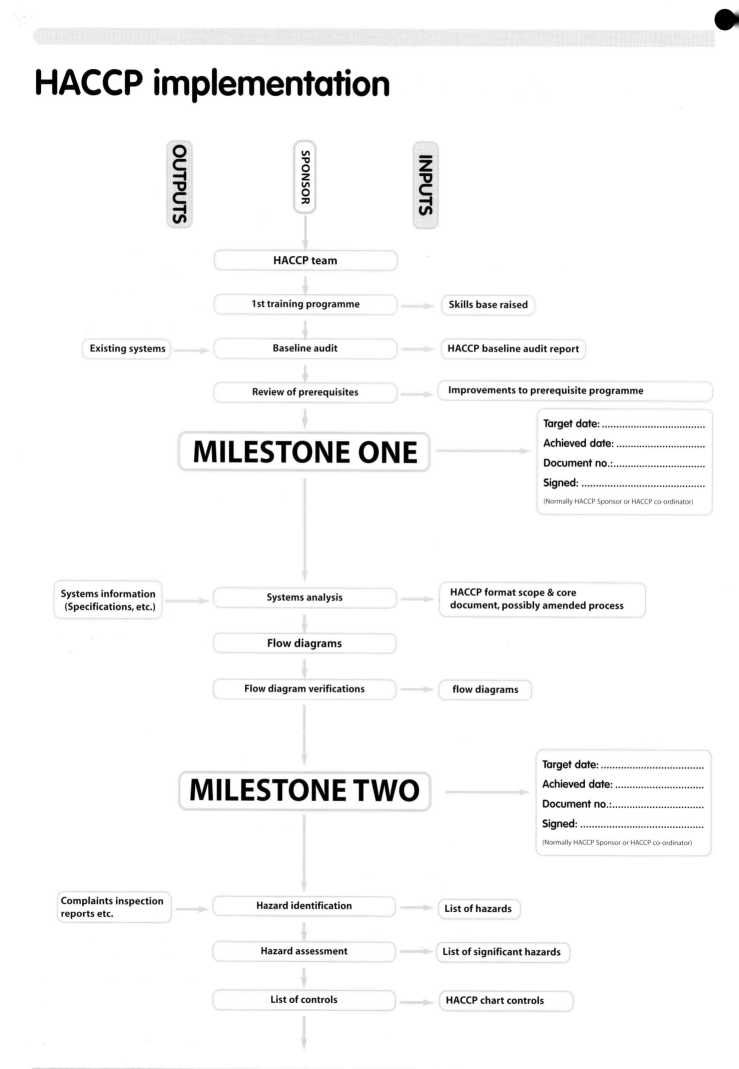

**OUTPUTS**

**SPONSOR**

**INPUTS**

HACCP team

1st training programme → Skills base raised

Existing systems → Baseline audit → HACCP baseline audit report

Review of prerequisites → Improvements to prerequisite programme

**MILESTONE ONE** →

Target date: ...............................
Achieved date: ...............................
Document no.: ...............................
Signed: ...............................
(Normally HACCP Sponsor or HACCP co-ordinator)

Systems information (Specifications, etc.) → Systems analysis → HACCP format scope & core document, possibly amended process

Flow diagrams

Flow diagram verifications → flow diagrams

**MILESTONE TWO** →

Target date: ...............................
Achieved date: ...............................
Document no.: ...............................
Signed: ...............................
(Normally HACCP Sponsor or HACCP co-ordinator)

Complaints inspection reports etc. → Hazard identification → List of hazards

Hazard assessment → List of significant hazards

List of controls → HACCP chart controls

# HACCP implementation

Identify CCPS ┈┈► CCPS on HACCP chart

## MILESTONE THREE

Target date: ...................................
Achieved date: ...............................
Document no.:...............................
Signed: ...........................................
(Normally HACCP Sponsor or HACCP co-ordinator)

Establish critical limits

Establish monitoring ┈┈► Monitoring S.O.P.

Establish corrective actions ┈┈► Corrective actions S.O.P.

Verification of HACCP plan

## MILESTONE FOUR

Target date: ...................................
Achieved date: ...............................
Document no.:...............................
Signed: ...........................................
(Normally HACCP Sponsor or HACCP co-ordinator)

Existing systems ┈┈► Establish review criteria/dates

HACCP application training

Complete documentation ┈┈► HACCP document

Amendment to post HACCP principles

## MILESTONE FIVE

Target date: ...................................
Achieved date: ...............................
Document no.:...............................
Signed: ...........................................
(Normally HACCP Sponsor or HACCP co-ordinator)

# Where do I start ?

These steps are not part of HACCP principles as established by Codex. If, however, an organisation is serious about the long-term success of its system, it is essential to consider the above, even if not following all the processes outlined. Some areas mentioned are covered in greater detail in the next section (Prerequisites of HACCP). If these processes are followed, the commencement of HACCP with Principle one (see *page 48*) will be much easier for the HACCP team.

## How do I launch HACCP ?

What has been covered so far should have given a picture as to the involvement in implementing HACCP and that a short timescale is not appropriate.

There is much debate as to how a HACCP system should be launched within a company: either phased over a relatively long period as each plan is completed; or launched on a specific date when the whole programme has been completed. There are benefits and disbenefits in both.

## Phased

This allows trial of the system as each product or process is launched. It aids the development of the HACCP team and allows a flexible finish date. It can, however, create problems with publicity and with instigating change within the company.

## Specific launch date

The problem here is that if it takes six months to the launch date, the first product is ready for review at the launch date, and may have changed. There is no chance for feedback or trial, but it does provide a launch for publicity purposes. This is often the only way with process led HACCP when nearly all processes have to be considered before a full product is covered.

I favour a balance between the two, to allow the maximum benefit from both systems. A launch date for phase one (when a significant percentage of products has been covered) allows publicity, the chance for feedback and a second completion date within a specified tight timescale. There is thus an adjustment period for change to be implemented stage by stage, with feedback being picked up by the HACCP team.

It is very much dependent on the company size and type of HACCP as to how feasible this is going to be.

Satisfactory completion at this stage allows progression to Principle one of the Codex HACCP stages (Section 9). It is necessary, however, to provide some additional detail on the prerequisite systems already mentioned, both for those who have no experience of them, or for HACCP teams considering the integration of HACCP. The following chapters serve this purpose.

# Prerequisites to HACCP

## HACCP and the management of safety

This section is designed to expand on the principle of parallel system convergence mentioned in Section 8, Where do I start? It examines the relation of HACCP to the general principles of hygiene management, and in particular the relationships of HACCP and other food safety documents or systems. These might include product specifications or food safety/food hygiene policies (referred to as a 'food safety policy' for the purposes of this chapter). This follows the idea of integration and 'joined up food safety management' already expounded.

The relationship with a food safety policy is of particular relevance as it is the other major of food safety management documents found in food companies. In most instances, it will pre-date the implementation of the HACCP system. It will contain the key responsibilities relating to food safety, and thus needs to be strongly linked to HACCP. If it does pre-date the HACCP, it will necessitate the rewriting of the policy to incorporate all areas of hygiene to HACCP principles. Otherwise two policies will exist, each with a different approach to food safety.

Some smaller companies may not have this extent of existing documentation, and if not they should consider the production of a brief food safety policy as a key support document for their HACCP.

The following is not an absolute rigid format for a safety policy. Most would possess this framework, however, following the principles of safety management. This should provide guidance to those who wish to integrate HACCP to an existing safety policy, or to those who decide to produce one to complement the HACCP.

I shall start by outlining the principles of hygiene management as I understand them, and then examine how some of these principles translate to the policy document and HACCP.

## The principles of safety management

The relationships of the principles of safety management are perhaps best illustrated by the means of a simple diagram.

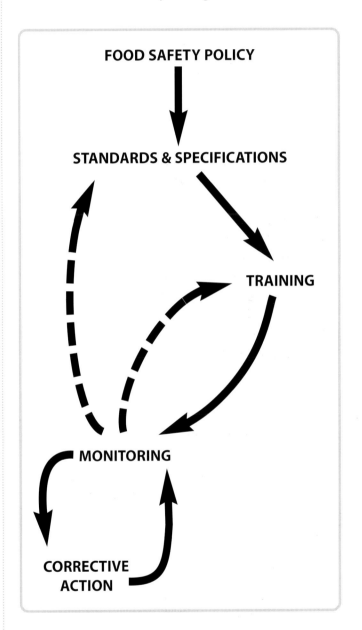

These principles effectively constitute the sections of a food safety policy. This will allow us to look at how these principles relate to HACCP, and the following table is provided to cover the likely crossovers that will exist between HACCP and safety policies. I shall then discuss some of these areas in more detail.

# Prerequisites to HACCP

| Safety Policy Section | HACCP Link | Discussion |
|---|---|---|
| **1.** Statement of intent | Terms of reference | Statement should include HACCP principles and sponsor of the HACCP programme |
| **2.** Responsibilities/ Arrangements | HACCP team | Include HACCP team and relate individuals' responsibilities to HACCP plan |
| **3.** Raw ingredient/product specifications | Ingredient specific hazards | Hazard plan should consider inherent hazards that may be illustrated by specification. Specification conformity is a control. All products must be covered by a HACCP plan; link to product or process led |
| **4.** Practices/premise standards | Good hygiene practice | GHP can be considered in the elimination of generic hazards |
| **5.** Operating procedures | Flow diagram | Practices in product manufacture must be considered in producing and verifying the flow diagram |
| **6.** Legislation | Controls/critical limits | All established critical limits must be within the limits applied by the relevant legislation |
| **7.** Training needs | HACCP team/staff training requirements | Training needs reviewing in light of the HACCP. The identified CCPs and related procedures become the basis of training hygiene, and HACCP skills require incorporating into training |
| **8.** Monitoring procedures | Monitoring of CCPs | CCPs redefine required monitoring points, level and frequency of monitoring. Monitoring should not be duplicated |
| **9.** Review | Review | Review procedures for HACCP and hygiene policy should be integrated |
| **10.** Complaints procedure | Verification/review | Complaints levels/types may initiate review of HACCP |
| **11.** Sampling procedure | Verification/review | Sampling results may initiate review of HACCP |
| **12.** Crisis management | Corrective action | Certain levels of deviation from the target level may initiate one of the crisis management scenarios |

Although there is not enough space to undertake a detailed discussion of each of the above areas (and not all will be applicable to every company), I have endeavoured to undertake examination of some of the most important areas below.

## Statement of intent

The statement of intent is a management led mission statement in relation to food safety. All too often such statements are legislation compliance based and not proactive. The production of the principles of HACCP will permeate all aspects of food safety and thus should be integrated with this statement, and the signatory of the statement of intent becomes the sponsor for the HACCP system. An example statement incorporating this ideal is provided below.

# Prerequisites to HACCP

'It is the intention of [company name] to produce safe, good quality food as demanded by our customers. To achieve this we will comply with all relevant legislation and take a proactive role in the prevention of complaints or legal contraventions by the implementation of a HACCP (Hazard Analysis Critical Control Point) system and associated procedures.

Everyone has responsibility for food safety, from me down throughout the company. [Company name] will endeavour to provide the means necessary (including materials and training) to ensure that all staff members can contribute effectively.

Signed:

..................................................................

**Managing Director'**

## Monitoring

Most companies, even small catering and retail outlets, undertake a significant amount of monitoring already; either as good practice or because of 'recommendations' made by enforcement officers. In many situations, this is haphazard and ill defined, and often a waste of time and resources. Because of the lack of framework for the monitoring it is often not carried out, or not actioned upon even if it is undertaken. The classic illustration to this will be familiar to many; refrigeration monitoring forms that are not filled in or read 5°C every day in the same coloured pen.

A combination of HACCP-related CCP monitoring and principles of safety management allows us to produce a hierarchy of structured monitoring that should then become integral to the food safety policy and can be incorporated in standard operating procedures and staff responsibilities. It provides a structure and purpose that makes the selling of monitoring to staff easier, and thus more necessary and effective.

What HACCP identifies is the minimum level of monitoring necessary for the safety of the product. Within the HACCP plan the procedure and frequency of monitoring needs to be set; this may already be the same as the existing monitoring, if not, it dictates a change in the existing procedure.

Unfortunately, despite the investment in training and specific work instruction this base level monitoring is often difficult to ensure. Non-conformance can generate extra work and interfere with production targets. The role of the supervisor in unrecorded checking is important but there is very much a need for checking at this level to be formalised, into a weekly checklist format. The main role of this structured

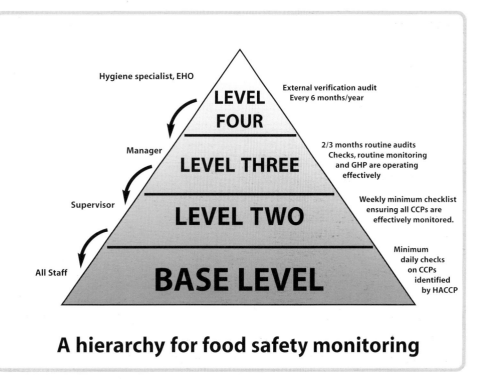

## A hierarchy for food safety monitoring

check is to ensure the base level CCP checks are being completed effectively. It also allows checks to be made on areas of good manufacturing practice that may not be monitored at the base level, such as cross-contamination prevention, structure and personal hygiene. In designing the form, simplicity should be the key to limit the time taken and thus encourage regular use.

There is also the need for in-depth auditing of the HACCP plan; this can take place internally as part of a third tier of inspection carried out by managers or hygiene specialists, (a first party audit) or externally, using consultants (or Environmental Health Officers). Such an audit is termed a third party audit if carried out by an external body or a fourth party audit when part of a regulatory role.

The frequency of such an audit is dependent on product risk and complexity, but every six months is normally the minimum. This tier of audit must check the validity of the whole HACCP system, and the efficiency of the second and third tier of monitoring.

Documentation of all these monitoring levels is necessary to enable review to be carried out, and to help demonstrate the adequacy of control in contributing to a 'due diligence defence'

In my opinion, the failure of integration of HACCP to existing systems is the primary reason for the medium-to long-term failure of HACCP within any organisation. The system is effectively built on poor support foundations and, although visually splendid, on completion it is apt to crumble once the spotlight is removed. For this reason the consideration of prerequisites becomes one of the most important steps in HACCP. As much as possible should be made of this by both management and the HACCP team. I am sure that much more research into best practice in this area will follow as its significance is realised, and it will receive greater emphasis within training materials.

# HACCP and ISO quality management

Quality Management is essentially the management of principles and procedures involved in ensuring that a company constantly produces products that uniformly meet the objectives they wish to achieve. Quality Management is a science in its own right and the following must be seen as a summary of how its ideas can help HACCP, not a full document on Quality Management.

In many instances, this will be formalised by one of the international standards that establishes procedures for Quality Assurance. The most common of these (certainly within the UK) is the International Organisation for Standards (ISO) 9000 series standards (24), and it is on the basis of this standard that the following comments are made. Whilst other standards may be applicable, this is the widest accepted standard and similar principles apply in them all.

The use of a formal Quality Management System does make sense; HACCP will ensure safety of the product, ISO 9000 will ensure that this level is consistently met. Without a HACCP system there may be consistent production of an unsafe product. Without quality principles a company may presume a HACCP system is working and act complacently in its use.

To proceed with a full ISO 9000 system does, however, have significant drawbacks; the main ones being the significant involvement of staff time and the extensive paperwork that is generated. It may be detrimental to create such a drain of money and resources at the same time as implementing HACCP. If an ISO system is not in place, it is recommended that full ISO accreditation is seen as a medium-term goal (three to five years), but that the principle of Quality Management is incorporated in

# Prerequisites to HACCP

HACCP at this stage. Not only does this produce better control over the HACCP system, but also creates a firmer platform for constructing a Quality Management System at a later date. In many premises full ISO accreditation is not achievable even in the long term, but this should not mean this approach is abandoned.

It is recommended that within any organisation a member of staff undergoes ISO 9000 Lead Assessor Training. In a small company, this may not be practicable and the following table is designed to provide an outline of the most important aspects of ISO 9000 that relate to HACCP. In a medium or large company, all HACCP team members should possess a working understanding of the following principles, irrespective of whether or not anyone has undergone the Lead Assessor Training.

There are significantly more principles that can be applied to HACCP and these can be found by reference to the ISO standard. The above are seen as the most important and

| Quality Management Principle | HACCP Implication |
|---|---|
| Document control | HACCP documentation is significant, and is constantly being updated. The dating of documents to ensure the 'live' document is identifiable and older ones removed is useful. A controlled number of documents to named people will aid this.<br>Document referencing with a referable number will aid cross-referencing. |
| Purchasing | Both system safety and quality are dependent upon the safety and uniform nature of incoming raw ingredients. It is therefore necessary to have specifications that are monitorable for incoming products. Where a specification covers safety this should be highlighted by the HACCP plan. |
| Traceability | Outgoing products should be labelled and recorded to enable batch-specific product recall.<br>Record of raw ingredient use should also be available to enable tracing of products should raw ingredient failure be identified.<br>Ideally there should be a trail to enable link between raw ingredient batches and final product codes. |
| Monitoring and testing | Where a CCP is identified then recorded monitoring should take place. The procedure for monitoring and for non-conformance parameters (i.e. the critical limits) should be clear and written. Equipment used should be suitable, accurate and not pose its own hazards. It should also be tested and calibrated and a record made. For example, probe thermometers should be disinfected prior to each use and calibrated monthly. |
| Non-conformance | In a situation where monitoring indicates a 'non-conformance', there should be a written procedure for its correction (i.e. the corrective action). There must always be a written record of non-conformance, and the associated corrective action. |
| Monitoring records | All monitoring forms at critical control points should be maintained in a retrievable form for a minimum of three years.<br>In some instances this is not practicable; there should however always be rapid access available to all monitoring forms for the shelf life of the given product, plus six months, as this can be seen as the maximum time that reference is likely to need to be made following identification of non-conformance. |
| Verification audits | Regular formal and recorded audits should be made of the system to illustrate its conformance to the written standard. Any variance must be recorded; the cause identified and then corrected.<br>This is part of the verification and validation process. |

# Prerequisites to HACCP

**Building an effective HACCP: 1 training of staff**

the most helpful in ensuring consistency and quality when implementing a HACCP system.

## HACCP and training

Training in relation to HACCP falls into three categories: product or process training; the hygiene training that is necessary to complete the HACCP; and specific training in HACCP skills.

The introduction of a HACCP system not only creates an additional training need within an organisation, it often calls into question the whole history of training hygiene.

To try to explain this statement one only needs to examine a company's training policy; this is generally based upon a perception of minimum legal compliance, and not on the HACCP system of the company. Thus, most meat processing premises, or sweet factories, are happy to send staff on a catering based level one (for example, Basic Food Hygiene) course that

bears little resemblance to their day-to-day work or the hazards they are likely to encounter. Yet a HACCP system goes a long way to identifying the training needs of a company and should form the basis of the objectives for such a training programme that will be far more effective than a routine qualification. Training in relation to HACCP often needs delivering at two points: first, in the early stages of development to raise the skills base to allow HACCP implementation; and second, more task specific training as the plan is being implemented to teach changes in monitoring or other procedures. Ultimately each company should undertake a full **training needs analysis** (TNA), which also assesses the current level of knowledge, and considers such areas as socio-economic background, level of intelligence and cultural and language learning barriers. The following will offer guidance and a structure in which the analysis will fit. At this stage it is probably advantageous to divide staff and examine their two training needs (hygiene and HACCP) together.

# Prerequisites to HACCP

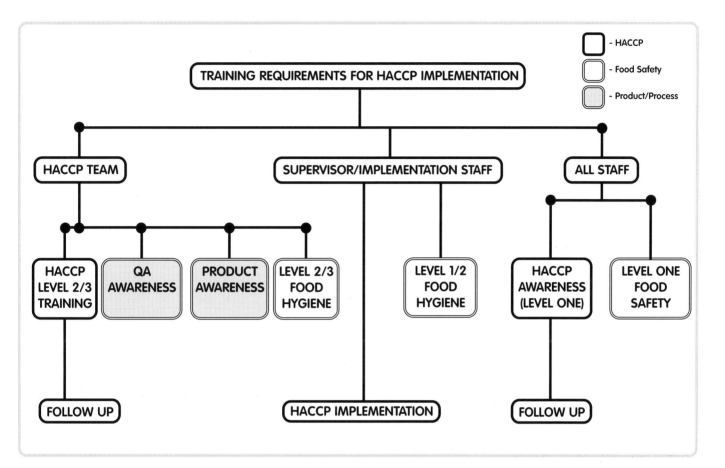

## HACCP team

Looking first at those staff who are going to be directly involved in the development of the HACCP plan (predominately the HACCP team and associated staff) there are three areas of training required: **technical training** in the product and process; **food hygiene training;** and **HACCP training.** It is often possible to combine skills of different team members, or to 'buy in' knowledge without undergoing additional training. However, the members of the team will all be able to make a better contribution if everyone is trained to a minimum level.

It is not to be assumed that everyone involved in HACCP has got adequate technical knowledge of the process being examined. Such a statement is particularly pertinent when any external 'expert' help is bought in. The easiest way of not creating any discomfort is to allow supervisors or operators to be involved in the HACCP team

and present technical information before each HACCP plan is approached.

It is necessary for the evaluation of hazards and identification of CCPs to have a detailed knowledge of food hygiene; all members should have minimum level two (Intermediate Food Hygiene or equivalent), with some members with level three (Advanced) or degree-related knowledge that will be an advantage to most medium to large companies. Without this training, there will be no understanding of, for example, the heat stable nature of some bacterial toxins that can affect the decision of criticality.

Any outsiders (for example, if you 'buy in' skills such as employing a product, Quality Assurance or HACCP specialist) should receive the product specific training that supervisors receive to be able to understand the hazards inherent in the particular process and premises. Even without external influence it is wise to provide internal product training to provide a level playing field in implementing the HACCP, so that decisions regarding a product are not made on the recommendation of one staff member.

Finally, it is often necessary to undergo training in HACCP, as even level three training only provides a technical insight and has little time to look at its practical application. The advantage of undergoing HACCP training is also that the members have a uniform approach to it, overcoming differences of presentation and approach that variable experience and past training may bring. There are various courses available. For caterers trying to meet the minimum legal requirement for self-regulation, probably with some limited documentation, then the Royal Society for the Promotion of Health *Certificate in Essential HACCP Practice*, is pitched at an ideal level.

Other courses include:

1. The Royal Institute of Public Health *Intermediate Certificate in HACCP Principles and their Application in Food Safety (31)* is compliant with the nationally recognised Training Standard. It is examined by multiple choice questions and questions related to a given scenario and gives a level two qualification that would serve to provide a reasonable level of knowledge for members of a HACCP team, or for a manager of a business implementing a documented HACCP system. The Level Two Chartered Institute of Environmental Health *Intermediate Certificate in Hazard Analysis (6)*.

2. The Chartered Institute of Environmental Health *HACCP in Practice* (5) or the The Royal Institute of Public Health *Advanced Diploma in HACCP Principles and their Application in Food Safety* are both minimum two-day level three qualifications. More formal and Codex

linked than The Royal Institute of Public Health Level Two certificate they serve well for: Owners/managers of manufacturing businesses; HACCP team leaders; Auditors of HACCP systems; and the HACCP trainers. The Chartered Institute of Environmental Health qualification is examined by the means of a work-based case study and thus benefits the commencement of HACCP within the premises as part of 'guided learning'. The Royal Institute of Public Health Diploma complies with the nationally recognised Training Standard at the Advanced level.

Reference can also be made here to the development of computer-based training packages on HACCP, in both the USA and UK.

This description of training requirements is satisfactory for those staff who have direct involvement in the HACCP team but is not practicable for a full workforce. However, all staff members require some awareness of the HACCP system, and this is unlikely to have been covered in their previous training. To some extent, therefore, the implementation of HACCP-related training is much easier on a new workforce (a 'green field' premises). In the majority of cases, the HACCP programme will be introduced to an existing workforce, and the retraining of all levels of staff to the above standard is not practicable. In such a situation, the updating of staff to introduce the necessary areas of HACCP is necessary.

Most companies would benefit from the following three levels of training:

### 1. All staff: HACCP awareness (2-4 hours)

A brief introduction to HACCP, the key principles and how they will be introduced into the company. How work practices will change and what specific responsibilities will be allocated to different levels of staff. Key terminology that staff may encounter in working documents should be introduced. This type of training should be developed in-house.

## 2. Staff involved in implementing areas of the HACCP plan/supervisors (4-6 hours)

This level of detail is particularly pertinent to those who have to undertake CCP monitoring, covering in more detail the hazards and controls specific to the company. Training should be as per the above level, plus coverage of monitoring and documentation requirements and procedures. Task specific actions to be taken in the event of an out-of-control situation (for example, an exceeded critical limit). The course can readily be tailored to different groups of staff.

## 3. Management (4-6 hours)

Summary of the principles of HACCP. Detail of the benefits of the HACCP system, how it is to be managed and the resource implications in the long and short term. Particular emphasis should be made of the marketing advantages.

Ideally, all staff should undergo the level of training relevant to them AND the level below. They should undertake the level below with the staff for whom they are responsible; showing involvement, reducing barriers between staff and receiving the same information as people they will directly supervise in undertaking HACCP. This approach to training is sometimes termed an 'inclusive training model'.

There are other locally/regionally produced courses, or those produced for specific sectors of the food industry that may meet some of these training requirements. These are of variable quality. Mention must be made here of the Meat and Livestock Commission 'Accelerated HACCP Programme' (26) that did a successful job of teaching HACCP principles (broadly) to managers of retail butchers. This must be seen as a particular success to increase practical knowledge to a sector of the industry that has been slow to respond to HACCP, and which could benefit most.

## General training requirements

The following is intended to illustrate the input and output of HACCP to general food hygiene training. This link is rarely made and yet hygiene training as a prerequisite to HACCP, and HACCP as the guiding idea in dictating training needs are obvious links to be made.

### Induction/hygiene awareness training

The requirements of this level of training to cover those practical areas that are essential in operating safely relate directly to CCPs and critical limits. The HACCP plan highlights those elements that are essential for safety, at what point in the process they are necessary and what limits need to be met. Without explaining the full complexity of HACCP, this can then be incorporated in training objectives that meet legal requirements and are company specific.

### Level one (e.g. basic level)

The same principle as above applies; the more targeted at the hazards and controls the HACCP identifies, the more valuable the training will be. Larger companies will benefit from courses tailored around the framework of a level one syllabus, either internally or by an external training organisation. Smaller companies should aim to undergo training as pertinent as possible to their industry sector, and frame this with support training that applies this to their own product and process.

Use of a modular training package such as the CIEH 'Food Hygiene Options' package is a step in the right direction. This package also has the advantage of having an elected module that can be used to give awareness of what HACCP is, which should also be an objective of this level of training that is not necessarily on the syllabus. On a 'need to know basis' this should only be an overview.

supervisors something against which to check; the phrase 'Good personal hygiene' is open to interpretation and cannot be monitored.

## Cleaning and disinfection

Whilst standards and procedures for cleaning should be related to hazards (for example, work surfaces used for high-risk foods require disinfecting), the use and management of cleaning is usually covered by a separate cleaning schedule. This states the cleaning procedure and frequency of areas to be cleaned, and allocates responsibility to a member of staff. In a high-risk situation, where contact with a work surface is inevitable, it is possible to set criteria for the monitoring of cleaning effectiveness, using swabs or adenosine triphosphate (ATP) analysis. The time for swab total viable count (TVC) results means this is rarely established as a CCP; and thus the procedure fits well with GHP.

## Specific physical contaminants

The normal contaminants of particular concern in low-risk manufacturing are glass, metal and wood. The production of a specific policy can, however, be created to deal with any contaminant that is of concern. The control of such hazards can be well addressed by HACCP, but most of these policies pre-date HACCP and exist as stand-alone documents. Using glass as the most widespread example, the policy would normally comprise the following:

1.  An inventory of glass and glass types found in each room or area.

2.  A policy statement on the exclusion or control of each type of glass (for example, the exclusion of glass drinking vessels or the use of shatterproof, filmed door glazing).

3.  A procedure for dealing with glass

breakage, and recording the incident to minimise the risk of contamination.

There are other examples of GHP, such as raw material handling, waste management, dispatch procedures, etc. but this should provide an insight into common examples and how they are significant.

# Raw ingredients/final product control

The initial stages of HACCP are essentially systems analysis. The scope of the HACCP plan, therefore, states the starting and finishing points of the HACCP, and these are usually the receipt of goods and delivery or retail sale of the finished product. This section is not supposed to duplicate this consideration in Principle One, but to offer discussion on areas where we do not have full control, but can exert influence, specifically, raw ingredients prior to receipt and the final product in the hands of the caterer or consumer. Critical control points can only be at points where we can effectively monitor, therefore HACCP cannot control the product fully prior to receipt, or once dispatched.

This can be illustrated by the following diagram.

## Raw ingredient control

Effectively this shows that however much control is exerted on a product during the period of direct influence, if the incoming raw ingredients have variable hazards, to an extent that cannot be foreseen and therefore controlled, then there will be hazards in the final product. Uniformity of raw ingredients allows the hazards to be identified (by specifying a partly processed product, for example), or to be dealt with later in the process. Thus, an envisaged problem of foreign material (stones, etc.) in flour can be addressed by sieving the incoming ingredients.

# Prerequisites to HACCP

Ensuring the consistent quality of incoming ingredients is one of the principles of ISO 9000 Quality Management, but again this can only be fully ensured at the point of delivery. There can be substantial debate as to the starting point of HACCP; I would favour delivery as the first point where absolute control is possible, and purchase/supplier assessment as part of a separate generic control. Where an intrinsic product hazard could exist that requires a control in its manufacture or distribution, the first dependable control (that is, the first monitorable point) over it is when it is delivered, even if the control is many process steps before.

The principle of control of incoming ingredients is sometimes referred to as

## Raw Ingredient/Final Product Control

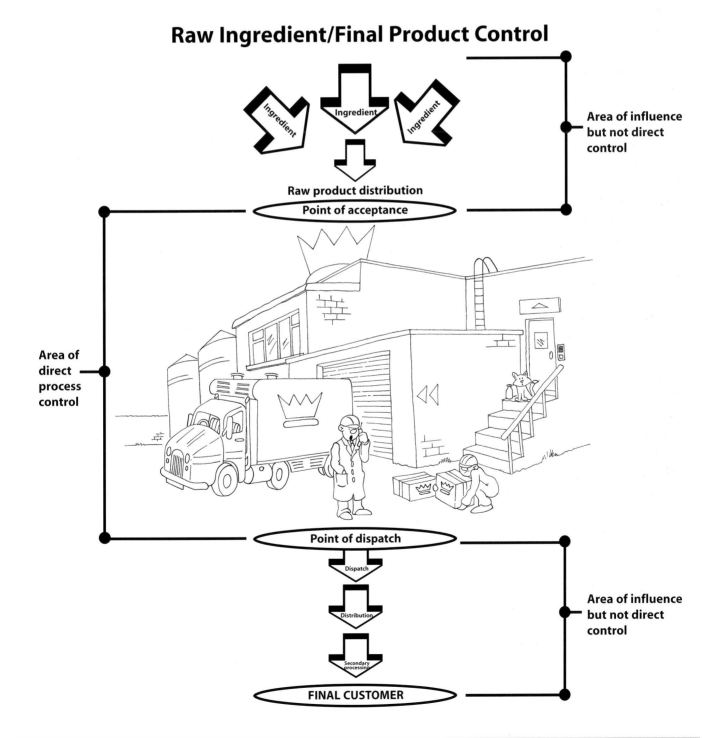

# Prerequisites to HACCP

## 1. Tolerance on limits (such as temperature and use-by dates)

Within the control of an organisation, the establishment of exact critical control limits (such as 3°C for cook-chill storage) is achievable. It would be naive and dangerous to expect this extent of control from the public. A similar statement could be made of reheating temperatures or 'use-by' dates. If every person who used a product a day out-of-date were to suffer food poisoning then the hospitals would be full. Therefore, some degree of tolerance must be built in to customer control parameters.

## 2. Labelling

Clear, visible labelling in plain language should highlight any necessary controls by the customer. For example, 'reheat for x minutes at setting y, stirring regularly until piping hot' has much more meaning to the public (who do not have a probe thermometer) than 'reheat to 80°C'.

## 3. Education

In situations where products are not labelled, or in conjunction with labelling education campaigns, leaflets or helplines can be used to try to increase customer awareness of safety issues. Good examples include those leaflets produced for retail butchers, or helplines on food safety set up by supermarkets.

There is obviously also a link here to the 'Some post-HACCP principles' section (see *page 87*) regarding complaint monitoring, as this may highlight a need for improved labelling or customer awareness.

## Approaching the HACCP plan

It is perhaps wise at this juncture to stop and reflect on what has been achieved so far. It may be demoralising to have read to this stage, and possibly implemented changes to this extent, and then to realise we have not yet covered even one of the seven key principles of HACCP.

To some extent, the hardest part is now completed; we should have the background, the skills and the supporting systems to produce an effective HACCP system. This will make the following stages easier to carry out, and make their long-term success much more likely.

As the implementation of HACCP progresses it is worth keeping in mind the key considerations we have highlighted so far; the issues of management support, management of the process, the integration of HACCP with existing systems and of the use of GHP to make the HACCP easier.

If HACCP is the vehicle we claimed it was in the "Where do I start?" section, then we should now be in that vehicle, pointing in the right direction, fuel gauge on full and aware of how to drive it. Have a nice trip.

---

**HACCP TEAM BUILDING?**

See the exercises for HACCP Team Building in EXERCISE TWO on *page 100*.

# Revision questions

## Part one: prerequisites

1.  **The HACCP sponsor is:**

    a) Always the chair of the HACCP team
    b) The originator of the HACCP scheme
    c) A company that provides funding for the HACCP scheme

2.  **Which of the following is NOT a good example of GHP?**

    a) A written personal hygiene standard
    b) Structural maintenance procedures
    c) Cooking and cooling logs
    d) Cleaning policy and schedule

3.  **Which of the following is true?**

    a) HACCP documentation is a legal requirement for all premises
    b) HACCP is the same as Quality Assurance
    c) HACCP is about controls at all stages of a process
    d) HACCP is a type of food safety management

4.  **HACCP originated from:**

    a) The NASA space programme
    b) The European Commission
    c) CODEX Alimentarius
    d) A response to a *Clostridium botulinum* outbreak in canned food

# Prerequisites to HACCP

## Add your notes here

| ACTION POINT | PAGE | COMMENT |
|---|---|---|
|  |  |  |
|  |  |  |

# Implementation

## The seven core principles of HACCP

We are now equipped to be able to address the seven core principles of HACCP as listed in CODEX. This text will approach these principles in the order cited by CODEX (1997) (8), and despite the sometimes quoted 'twelve (or fourteen!) steps to HACCP' we will address any steps within these headings. I must add that direct reference is not made to CODEX in wording, and that some significant changes have been made. If you want the CODEX wording, go to the CODEX document.

We are going to examine the process that is effectively the carrying out of a **HACCP study,** and will culminate in a number of **HACCP plans.** The HACCP plan is the document that provides the written summary of the HACCP study. Normally it consists of a cover sheet or sheets, a flow diagram and a HACCP chart or CCP summary for each product or process. It does not normally contain the associated prerequisite documentation previously examined, but should refer to it wherever necessary.

One should consider all principles and understand them as a whole since they are all related and have no effect in isolation. The completion of each principle is a logical point for review and evaluation before progression to the next. The principles are far from even in respect of the amount of work they generate. Principle one, with a number of stages involved, constitutes about half the time of the exercise. Principles one and two pose the greatest technical difficulty and thus confusion.

I have endeavoured in the following to, first, provide the technical definition of what the principle is, and, second, to offer advice on its practical implementation and integration. Key words are explained in the glossary, 'Jargon busting'. Whilst the descriptions follow CODEX principles, variations and simplifications have been made. The examples given relate to both product specific and process led HACCPs, but it should be reiterated that there are many different ways of applying the HACCP principles, depending on the nature and extent of production.

**Building an effective HACCP: 3 implementation**

# The seven core principles of HACCP

## Principle one: the analysis of hazards

Principle one is extensive and is normally cited as having a number of subsections or steps. There are six discussed, but the way they are broken down varies in other texts or training materials. The culmination of this principle should be a structure for the HACCP plan, a completed scope of the plan, verified flow diagram, and the completion of identified hazards and controls (or preventive measures) on the HACCP plan summary. Ideally, any hazards that can be eliminated by a change in process or working practice should have been removed and/or minimised. If mistakes are made here in the representation of the process, or the omission of hazards, the rest of the principles will produce an invalid HACCP.

This principle should, therefore, illustrate compliance with the initial two principles of Regulation 4 (3) of the Food Safety (General Food Hygiene) Regulations 1995; the identification of hazards and where they occur in the process.

## Step one: the HACCP team

We have discussed aspects of the HACCP team make-up under training, and in the approach to resourcing the HACCP study. The skill base here is crucial to the successful completion of the plan.

Within a large organisation, the norm would be to have a core **HACCP team,** containing a nominated chairperson or facilitator. Part of the role of the facilitator is to communicate with the **HACCP sponsor.** A HACCP sponsor may have no role in the day-to-day workings of the HACCP team, but is the person who initiates the HACCP process, finances it, and has ultimate responsibility for it and liaises with the board/owners/directors.

Different HACCP plans in different sectors

of the same premises may employ additional specialists in different skills. Effectively, there is a hierarchy of team members; a core team who have key skills

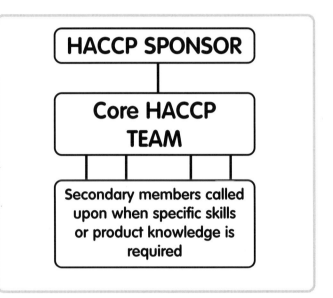

that must be present, and a second tier of staff who are called upon when specific skills may be required either on specific plans or specific steps in the plans.

**Core team members**
• **HACCP skills:** someone must have the expertise and experience of the application of HACCP techniques. Ideally, this should be someone within the company who also has other necessary skills. It may be possible to buy in these skills as a consultant but internal application is always best for the long-term efficiency of the system.

• **Management skills:** at least one member should have access to decision-making powers at a high level to ensure the instigation of change where necessary, and to fund the change. This person will normally have project and team management skills to oversee the HACCP team, facilitate their involvement, and act as an arbitrator if needed. This person is often termed a HACCP Co-ordinator or Facilitator.

# The seven core principles of HACCP

• **Quality management skills:** all members should be familiar with the principles of Quality Management. Ideally, one member should receive Lead Assessor Training.

• **Technical skills:** in-depth knowledge of the industry sector being dealt with is essential.

• **Site experience:** someone must have practical experience of the operating systems and standard of the site being addressed.

As long as these skills are evenly addressed, the formal make-up of the core team cannot be dictated. As an example, a core HACCP team for a large manufacturing bakery is outlined below.

For core members, attendance at meetings of the HACCP team is seen as essential. Due to sickness/holidays, etc. this may not always be possible and thus it is recommended that a reserve name is available from each of the relevant teams, and that this person is kept briefed as to developments.

There will then be the second tier of staff who can be called on at different stages (for example, laboratory manager when needed during consideration of monitoring) or for different products (for example, production manager, bread products). This will vary depending on the product type and size of organisation but to give an illustration of possible considerations, the list of staff drawn up for a large manufacturing bakery is given below.

Production Manager
(Bread products)
Production Manager
(Confectionery – non cream)
Production Manager
(Confectionery – cream)
Laboratory Manager
Maintenance Engineer
Cleaning Supervisor
Training and Personnel Manager

Once assembled, the team can then progress to step two. If the staff have never worked together, it may be wise to start with some type of team building prior to the involvement directly in HACCP. This could consist of training together, or involve a 'time-out' session with the sole aim of team building. The exercises in the section 'Exercise two' are designed to be used for this purpose.

---

**HACCP TEAM BUILDING?**
See the exercises for HACCP Team Building in EXERCISE TWO on *page 100*.

---

## Core HACCP Team for a Large Bakery

| | |
|---|---|
| **Susan Oaks** (Hygiene Manager) | **HACCP Team Co-ordinator** <br> HACCP skills, access to decision-making |
| **Frank Aston** (Production Manager) | Technical and site experience skills <br> Quality management training |
| **Harold Smith** <br> (Product Development Manager) | Technical and site experience skills <br> Quality management training |
| **Henry Owen** <br> (Quality Assurance Manager) | Technical and site experience skills <br> Quality management training <br> Some HACCP experience |

# The seven core principles of HACCP

## Step two: the terms of reference of the HACCP

HACCP is an ill-defined tool and we have already seen the differences. In essence, this step is a means of stating the type and extent of HACCP to be used. It may therefore be partially imposed on the HACCP team by the sponsor, but nevertheless should be agreed by the HACCP team and recorded.

The primary statements that should be covered by the terms of reference are:

**1.** The type of HACCP plans that are to be produced. This is normally a statement that the HACCP is product specific, process led or generic; or a described combination.

**2.** How the HACCP study is going to be presented. Any protocols, particularly relating to the use of a Quality Management system such as ISO 9000, which are to be used.

**3.** The types of hazards to be considered by the HACCP team and thus addressed by the HACCP study. In most situations, this will be a statement that the HACCP plan covers microbiological, physical and chemical hazards.

**4.** Whether or not quality issues are to be addressed by the team. If not, how are they to be differentiated from safety issues within the HACCP study?

**5.** With regard to safety control, it must be decided at what point in the whole process that control can be exerted, and whether safety is dependent on any later stage in the process. The relationship of this HACCP study to any others, for example, if a product such as chocolate is then used within the same company to make chocolate enrobed bars at a different site.

These terms of reference should be held in sight at all later stages of the process, and should be used to indicate if the team is digressing. They are key principles and must be fully understood by all team members. Most important is the targeting of safety and it should be advised in the early stages of a HACCP team that safety is the only concern, with quality issues added at a later stage.

## Step three: the scope of the HACCP study

The HACCP team skills in relation to technical issues are important here. A full understanding of the product and process is necessary. This part is often referred to as the 'scope' of the HACCP plan, as it offers a written description of what it is for, how it relates to other products and how the product is to be packaged and used. Technically, a HACCP scope normally also contains information from the above terms of reference stage.

This written description is important for a number of reasons. First, it gives the HACCP team, in a referable format, the product knowledge for the process/product under examination. Second, it allows others to understand what is covered by the given plan, and how this relates to other products and processes. Third, it gives reference to specification, packaging, ingredients, processing techniques, labelling and intended use (including any susceptible target groups) that are important in the making of decisions regarding hazards.

The following example provides an illustration of 'terms of reference and scope of the plan'. The amount of detail obviously varies depending on the nature and risk of the given product.

> **HACCP TEAM BUILDING?**
> See the exercises for HACCP Team Building in EXERCISE TWO on *page 100*.

# SPEEDiBURGER FAST FOOD RESTAURANTS

**HACCP PLAN – 1/4 lb Beefburgers**

## TERMS OF REFERENCE

The following is a HACCP (front sheets, flow diagrams and plans) for the production of 1/4 lb beefburgers. It is a plan to be used for only this product. Size of product and reference should be made to other plans for other products.

Managers/Franchisees *may not* vary the ingredients or ingredient specifications, or the recorded parameters in this HACCP plan, without prior written approval from the Central Product Quality Co-ordinator.

The attached plan was finalised on

........................................................................
by the HACCP co-ordinating team

**Ralph Borgen** *Central Product Quality Co-ordinator*

**Jemma Arkwright** *Brand Manager*

**Angela Smith** *Area Manager West*

**Frank Delaney** *Branch Manager, Cardiff*

**HACCP plans consider physical, chemical and microbiological hazards.**

## SCOPE OF THE PLAN

This plan covers stages from receipt of raw ingredients to the service of the finished product to either a take-away or restaurant guest who is the final consumer. Stages identified on the attached flow diagram include cooking of the burger, preparation and assembly of the final product.

Ingredients are stored under either ambient, refrigerated or frozen conditions as considered suitable and identified in the HACCP plan.

The finished product is served hot in a disposable clean, food grade container to the general public for immediate consumption without any further processing.

| INGREDIENT DETAILS | |
|---|---|
| 1/4 lb frozen beefburgers product | Spec Sp 031/00 |
| Pre-sliced sesame-seeded bun | Spec Sp 017/00 |
| Cooking oil (vegetable) | Spec Sp 039/00 |
| Pre-washed Iceberg lettuce | Spec Sp 04/00 |
| Onion | No written specification |
| Chilli sauce* | Spec Sp 059/00 |
| Sliced pickles* | Spec Sp 055/00 |

**\* Products used only at customer request.**

# The seven core principles of HACCP

## Step four: process flow diagrams

A process flow diagram is simply a diagrammatic representation of the stages involved in producing a product. Whilst it must progress logically, relate to how the product is actually produced and be complex enough to allow an understanding of the process, there is no absolute format to follow. However, the choice of format is important; many flow diagrams fail due to one or more of the following reasons, and it is worth considering these issues when drawing up and checking your own flow diagrams:

* The diagram is not complex enough to understand the process; it groups process steps together or omits ingredients.

* The diagram is too complex and not easy to understand. This can often be the case with the use of certain types of flow diagram and with the inclusion of too much non-product detail, such as packaging, materials and utensils.

* The diagram does not include all possible permutations of product flow. Common examples include ignoring the possibility of additional holding stages, reworking or reversing the processing order.

* The diagram is not representative of what really happens; either it has not been verified or the HACCP team do not have realistic site specific knowledge.

The simplest type of flow diagram is a **linear process step diagram.** This will only work with simple products with few ingredients. It does not have the complexity to show hazards from different ingredients, but is easy to produce. Effectively, it is a description of how a product is produced chronologically, broken into logical stages.

In teaching it, therefore, the student has only to write down how they do the process in detail and then group steps under general headings. The following example is chosen from a butcher's where this simplified approach was employed by the MLC (Meat and Livestock Commission) 'accelerated HACCP training' (26).

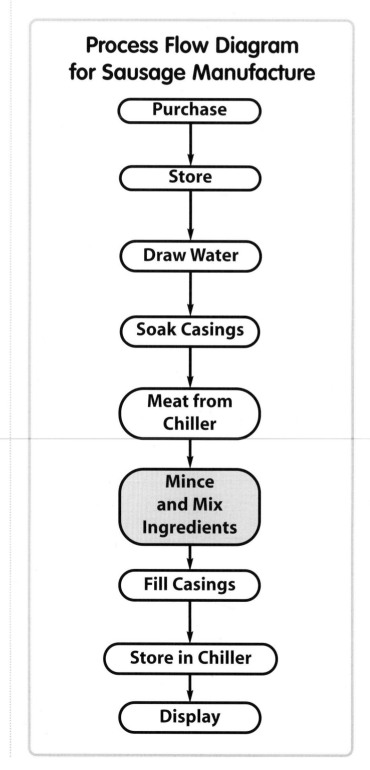

**Process Flow Diagram for Sausage Manufacture**

Purchase

Store

Draw Water

Soak Casings

Meat from Chiller

Mince and Mix Ingredients

Fill Casings

Store in Chiller

Display

# The seven core principles of HACCP

The evident disadvantage of such an approach is that hazards due to specific stages in preparation are not displayed, and the interaction of different process steps is not illustrated. In addition, confusion is caused because consideration is not made of process steps occurring in parallel.

For this reason the most commonly used type of flow diagram keeps ingredients, or groups of similar ingredients, separate until they are combined. This is a more realistic interpretation of what actually happens, and is relatively easy to do (with a little practice). This type of flow diagram will be used in examples as the norm from here. The starting point is to list ingredients along the top, and end with the finished product in the bottom and middle. Process steps for the product are centralised simple boxes joined by arrows. There is no need to provide detail of the action in each process step (such as 'cook at 75°C for two minutes, stirring regularly and check with probe thermometer') as this is provided later if necessary. The label 'cook' will suffice. Relatively cheap computer packages (such as Corel Draw) are available that make the graphic production of these relatively easy.

The following example for the production of a meat pie is taken from a medium-scale manufacturer and is intended to illustrate a realistic expectation of this type of premises.

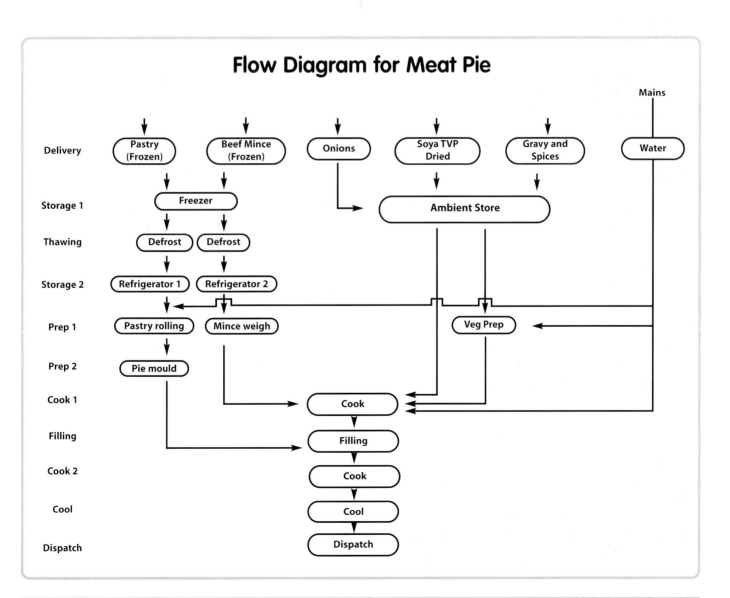

**Flow Diagram for Meat Pie**

## QSA Flow Diagram

### Safety study: Burger manufacture for 2 x 4 burgers

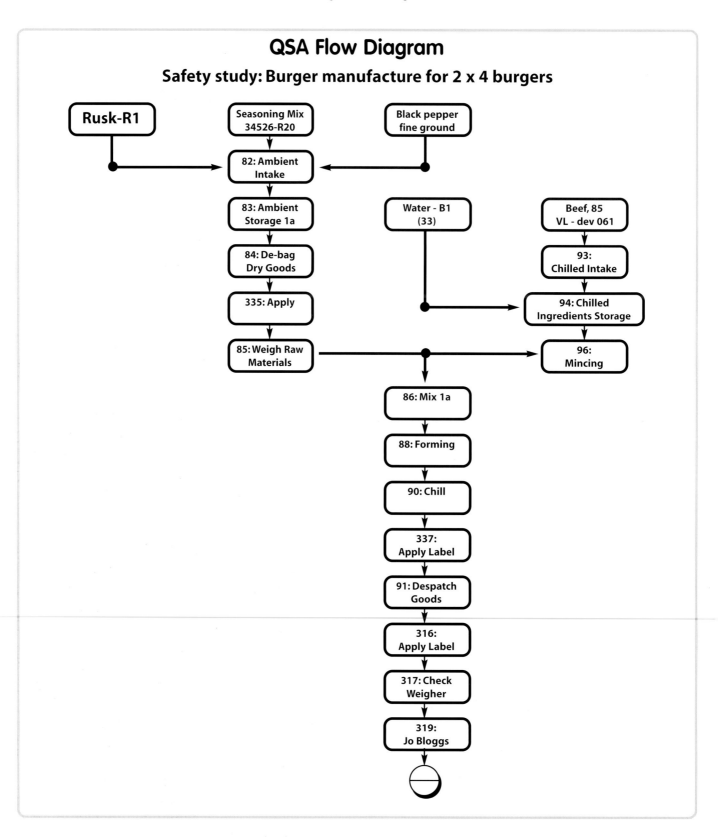

The above example is taken from the QSA HACCP computer package *(30)* and illustrates the complexity that can be represented in a flow diagram in a large-scale manufacturing environment. It can be seen that more process detail is evident, and, thus, significantly more process steps are identified.

# The seven core principles of HACCP

It is worth detailing a number of protocols for this type of flow diagram. Some of these can be seen in the previous pages examples.

1. All ingredients are listed along the top of the paper, with the final product centralised at the bottom.

2. If water used in washing or cooking is not listed as an ingredient, it is indicated as entering a process step in the following way:

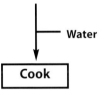

3. Layout should be such that lines do not have to cross. In a situation where this is unavoidable, the use of the following protocol indicates that the ingredient bypasses and is not incorporated in the product:

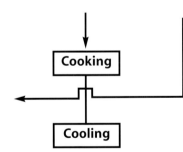

4. Numbering or naming of the process steps allows ease of transfer of data onto the HACCP plan. If a process step name is repeated (e.g. preparation), this should be labelled differently (e.g. 'cooked preparation' or 'preparation two'). This avoids confusion at later stages.

5. Any backward flow or reworking must also be identified on the flow diagram, as per the example illustrated:

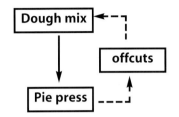

6. The flow diagram can be used to provide a summary of the whole HACCP study; with hazards identified by the use of dots for example, and the CCPs indicated by the use of colour or double boxing:

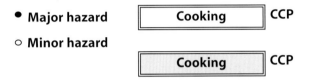

7. The flow diagram should be food centred but wherever packaging etc. enters the process, and may pose a hazard, this can be included. This should not cause confusion related to the product and sometimes a different font or colour is used.

On completion of the flow diagram, the HACCP team should endeavour to ensure that the diagrammatic representation is true to the practice on the factory floor. This can be done by following the product through ('walking the line') and by seeking verification from staff members involved in the particular line. Once this is completed, only then should the diagram be verified and passed as a ' live' document for progression to later stages. This should be the date recorded on the flow diagram, as shown in the example above. If the walk through indicates variances then these must not be ignored, but should form the basis of an updated flow diagram.

Often in a large factory environment, the flow diagram is completed by the use of a computer package, often with its own protocols of presentation (see Section 13).

# The seven core principles of HACCP

There are examples of more complicated process flow diagrams that include a diagrammatic representation of the nature of each process step, or that include coded diagrammatic representations for the movement of staff, utensils, waste, etc. In the vast majority of situations, I find these to be overcomplicated.

## Step five: the identification of hazards and related controls

A hazard is something that has the potential to cause harm. This may be **physical** (a foreign body, such as a piece of wood), **chemical** (contamination of a product with cleaning chemicals or pesticide residues), **biological** (naturally poisonous plants and animals) or more often than not **microbiological** (bacteria or their toxins, viruses, mycotoxins, saxitoxins, parasitic protozoans, etc.). All types of hazards should be assessed, dependent on the scope of the HACCP. Raw ingredient (intrinsic) hazards should not be forgotten, and can be incorporated into the HACCP plan stages or considered as a separate stage.

It is not proposed to cover all hazards within this manual as different industry sectors have different types and extents of hazards; thus, detailed product knowledge within the HACCP team is necessary. For example, the majority of sweet manufacturers are primarily concerned about wood as a physical contaminant; cake manufacturers may be concerned about ochratoxin and aflatoxin contamination of raw ingredients; cooked meat manufacturers by contrast are primarily concerned with salmonella and *E. coli O157*. This will require inclusion in the scope as wood contamination can be considered of little risk to human health.

In assessing hazards, the best initial method is for the HACCP team to list all potential hazards, using knowledge of the process. No assessment should be made of severity or extent at this stage; simply note down all the hazards. Enough detail must be given to enable adequate control to be listed. Stating 'microbiological' is not enough as there is a variety of controls (temperature control, stopping contamination) that depend on the nature of the microbiological hazard. Neither is there a need to list all the possible bacteria that pose a hazard if the control needed (such as thermal processing/cooking) is the same. Statements such as 'microbiological contamination', or 'microbiological survival' are therefore of the correct depth.

As well as using knowledge available in the enclosed environment of the HACCP team, other information should be obtained to identify potential hazards, as those closely involved in a process often become blind to hazards. The following are some that may be employed:

**1. Sample result analysis/complaint analysis and investigation.** Ultimately, hazards that are realised will be picked up either by routine analysis or by customer complaints. This can very usefully illustrate hazards that are not perceived by staff.

**2. Imposing the flow diagram on a premises plan.** Imposing a process flow diagram over a plan of the premises can illustrate where product movement could cause cross-contamination. It might illustrate unnecessary movement of the product, allowing redesign or changes in the process to reduce or eliminate hazards. This is one of the under-used advantages of HACCP flow diagrams.

**3. Raw ingredient specifications.** Analysis of lists of raw ingredients, and relevant data from suppliers will help to identify the inherent hazards in incoming products. This may have already been done as part of raw product safety assessment (see section 'Raw

# The seven core principles of HACCP

ingredient/Final product control').

**4. Inspection.** One of the best means of hazard identification is inspection, following the product in a 'downstream' direction (from raw ingredients to final product). External bodies will follow this protocol, so documentation from external customer audits and enforcement officer visits will highlight hazards identified.

The above processes will identify a large number of hazards, some of which are insignificant, some of which are already adequately addressed by good hygiene practice. It therefore becomes necessary to make an assessment so that the significant hazards can be addressed. This procedure is called Risk Assessment and does not necessarily constitute a legal part of hazard analysis in Regulation 4 (3). The criteria set here will play a significant role in the identification of critical control points later, and it is suggested that a structured approach is made in this assessment.

There are two considerations in the assessment of hazards, and these are the severity of the hazard if realised (severity of illness or injury, likelihood of fatality and likelihood of spread) and the risk of the hazard being realised (influenced by the occurrence, the number of products produced and the vulnerability of the target audience).

In most instances, the above assessment can be made from experience; and the following matrix is intended to illustrate an example of such an assessment. The decision on inclusion here will relate to the scope of the HACCP.

The following example is for a large range of product and hazard types and is purely for illustration purposes. The decision on likelihood will obviously vary in each situation encountered, considering the product, product frequency, premises layout, target group and effectiveness of current good hygiene practice.

The range highlighted in bold is that area to be considered in this situation as warranting inclusion in the CCP decision tree; termed significant hazards.

## Hazard Matrix Table

|  | LOW Likelihood | MEDIUM Likelihood | HIGH Likelihood |
|---|---|---|---|
| LOW Severity | Crystal formation in canned grapefruit | Wood in gelatin-based sweets | **Grain weevils in flour** |
| MEDIUM Severity | Glass in PET bottled drinks | ***Staphylococcus aureus* from ambient buffet** | **Salmonella in raw shell egg mayonnaise** |
| HIGH Severity | ***Clostridium botulinum* in canned soup** | **Aflatoxin in imported pistachio nuts** | **VTEC from consumption of raw beefburgers** |

# The seven core principles of HACCP

There is a number of formal rating schemes for the categorisation of severity of hazard, most notably from the US National Academy of Science (1969) *(27)* and the US National Research Council (1985) *(28)*. Based upon these, the following is only provided as a suggestion for consideration; as long as you apply your hazard criteria uniformly, your own rating will suffice.

## High severity hazards

VTEC, *Clostridium botulinum, Salmonella typhi and paratyphi, listeria monocytogenes,* shigella, hepatitis A, some heavy metals (for example, mercury), some chemicals (for example, bleach), some fish toxins (ciguatera) and injection needles.

## Medium severity hazards

Most salmonellae, campylobacter, vibrio, *E. coli* (except VTEC), *Staphylococcus aureus,* viral food poisoning, *bacillus spp.,* scombrotoxin, glass, stones and metal, some chemicals.

## Low severity hazards

Most foreign bodies (hair, cigarette ends, wood, etc.).

Using this type of rating allows us to assess the significance of hazards and to eliminate those that are not significant. The HACCP will then target significant hazards and not be overrun with remote and insignificant hazards. However, consideration must be made of the possibility of cumulative effects of hazards, from step to step in making such an assessment, or the combined effect of a number of hazards.

## Controls

Having identified the significant hazards, the associated control measures should be listed. A control is effectively something that

---

**Date: 2nd Jan 2001**
**Document Ref 02/0AB**

## HACCP Plan for Beef and Onion Pie

| No | Process Step | Food Safety Hazard | Hazard Significance | | | Control | CCP Decision | | | |
|---|---|---|---|---|---|---|---|---|---|---|
| | | | SEVERITY | RISK | SIGNIFICANT | | Q1 | 2 | 3 | 4 |
| 1 | Delivery | Microbiological contamination | H | L | Y | 1. Delivery only from approved suppliers | | | | |
| | | Physical contamination | L | L | N | 2. Temp of delivery vehicle | | | | |
| 2 | Ambient storage | Physical contamination | L | L | N | 1. Prerequisite structure and pest control programmes | | | | |
| 3 | Refrigerated storage | Microbiological growth | H | L | Y | 1. Temperature of cold holding unit 2. Use-by date on package | | | | |
| 4 | Preparation pastry | Microbiological contamination | H | L | Y | 1. Prerequisite cleaning & personal hygiene programmes | | | | |
| | | Physical contamination | L | L | Y | 2. Prerequisite cleaning programme | | | | |
| 5 | Meat preparation | Microbiological contamination | H | L | Y | 1. Cleanliness of equipment and utensils | | | | |
| 6 | Combine | Microbiological contamination | H | L | Y | 1. Cleanliness of equipment and utensils | | | | |

**H=HIGH  L=LOW  Y=YES  N=NO**

is designed to eliminate, or reduce any hazard to an acceptable limit. This serves to identify current controls in the assessment of criticality, and provides the basis for what controls need specifying at critical points later. There should be some type of control for all the hazards identified, but there may be more than one control for any one hazard.

There is no need to state detail here of limits, as this will be done at the critical limit stage if necessary.

## Step six: process amendment

Previous mention has been made of this in relation to process flow diagrams and the assessment of hazards, and the question reappears within the CCP decision tree. However, I prefer to formalise this as a separate stage in principle one as it is under-used, and one of the failings of many HACCP systems. Without the possibility of system amendment, HACCP can end up placing excessive control and monitoring on a poor system. Very often, these can be removed by simple amendments.

Application of logic and common sense at this stage will often allow hazards to be either eliminated or reduced so that they are not significant. This could be done by a change in work practice (providing a refrigerator adjacent to a preparation area to reduce time at ambient), an alteration of the order of processing (thermal processing at a later stage to eliminate hazards of contamination) or the substitution of a safer alternative ingredient (for example, pasteurised egg instead of shell egg). This is one of the neglected skills in HACCP and should be highlighted more within the seven core principles expounded by CODEX.

It is at this point that information is entered onto a HACCP plan or plans to illustrate the compliance with the seven principles. The process steps are listed and should correspond with the order or numbering given on the process flow diagram.

The identification of the controls constitutes the final stage in principle one and is the first milestone along the path of completing the HACCP. It is therefore recommended that the HACCP team formally verify and approve the hazard analysis before there is progression to principle two: the identification of critical control points. This should not mean it could not be amended as the procedure progresses, merely that this is the raw material on which the whole HACCP is based, and if this is inadequate, the whole HACCP will be flawed.

> **HACCP TEAM BUILDING?**
> See the exercises for HACCP Team Building in EXERCISE TWO on *page 100*.

# The seven core principles of HACCP

# Revision questions

## Part two: principle one

1.      Which of the following is the most important core HACCP team skill?

a)  Product awareness
b)  Microbiological sampling methods
c)  Cleaning schedules
d)  Degree in food technology


2.      A process flow diagram is:

a)  A chart to show responsibilities in the HACCP team
b)  A diagrammatic representation of a process
c)  A computer program
d)  A chart to summarise hazards and controls

3.      In identifying hazards at a process step, HACCP team members should:

a)  Always follow suggestions from the HACCP co-ordinator
b)  Concentrate on microbial hazards
c)  List a full variety of hazards from a variety of sources

4.      Which of the following is NOT part of  principle one?

a) A process flow diagram
b) Establishing verification procedures
c) Assembling the HACCP team
d) Identifying hazards

# The seven core principles of HACCP

## Add your notes here

| ACTION POINT | PAGE | COMMENT |
|---|---|---|
| | | |

New College Nottingham
Learning Centres

# The seven core principles of HACCP

## Principle two: critical control points

The decision on criticality of any process step is perhaps the most confused and confusing aspect of HACCP. If Principle one is the longest principle then without doubt Principle two is the hardest for people to understand. There is a number of definitions offered for critical control points, and a variety of means to find them. The logical starting point is the definition offered by CODEX *(8)*.

**'A step where control can be applied and is essential to prevent, eliminate or reduce a food safety hazard to acceptable levels.'**

There have been many different definitions offered, and many are more complicated. I find this definition offers a comprehensive and comprehensible understanding. In effect this means that we have to have effective control at this point or the hazard is likely to be realised. Omitting a control or allowing a control to fail at this point is likely to render the whole objective of the HACCP plan invalid. If we fail to identify a CCP then we do not exert the necessary control and the final product is likely to be unsafe. If we identify too many CCPs, we end up with the real CCPs clouded and, in effect, we have produced a manual of non-targeted good practice that does not highlight safety. Either way the system is likely to fail.

In CODEX, the decision on criticality is made using a **decision tree**. This comprises a number of sequenced questions which are applied at each process step identified by the flow diagram to reach a conclusion on criticality. The series of questions is applied for each hazard, as it is not necessary to identify all hazards at a process step as critical just because one hazard makes it so. The structured nature of the decision tree is designed to provide uniformity in decision-

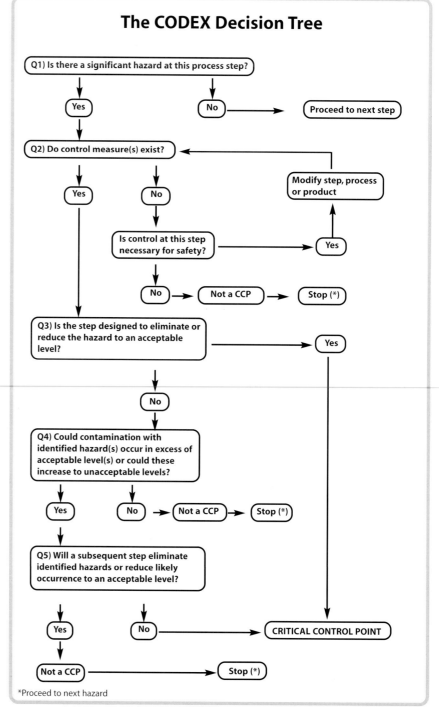

**The CODEX Decision Tree**

*Proceed to next hazard

making. The problem with the CODEX decision tree is that it is very complex and difficult to follow, and the questions are open to interpretation, different members of the same team may reach different conclusions (this makes an interesting exercise for any HACCP team). The decision tree should also be applicable to any hazard but is more difficult to follow for physical and chemical hazards than for microbiological hazards, consequently we have to approach the decision tree sensibly and use it with caution. Decision trees are not the only way to reach an outcome on criticality, a fact accepted even by CODEX. The following decision tree is based on the one in CODEX but with some simplifications and amendments.

If we explore each of these questions briefly, they are as follows:

### 1. Is there a hazard at this process step?

If there is no significant hazard there is nothing that needs control, and thus the process step is not a CCP. However, it is rare for a HACCP team not to identify some hazards of significance at a process step.

### 2. Do control measures for this hazard exist at this process step?

The final stage of hazard analysis is the identification of controls relating to the hazard. If there are no related controls, it is possible to proceed to the next question.

If there are related controls at this stage then a supplementary question (2a) is designed to bring into consideration the position of later controls to address the hazards, although these must then become CCPs. It also allows the removal of quality-related controls that are not relevant to food safety.

If the questioning identifies that control is necessary for food safety at this point, but there are no control measures, then the

process will need amending to bring it under control here or at a later stage. For example, the hazard of Salmonella is identified at the delivery stage of coconut to a sweet factory, but there is no later thermal processing and no checks made at the point of delivery. We can provide a later thermal processing step, purchase pasteurised coconut, remove coconut from the ingredients or input controls such as positive release on receipt of a test certificate for Salmonella. We then re-address question 2.

### 3. Is the process step designed to remove the hazard?

If a process step is designed to remove a hazard or reduce it so that it is not hazardous, this is obviously a CCP. Thermal processing is the best example. If the step is not so designed, we have to progress to see if the hazard will be removed later in the process.

### 4. Could contamination occur to cause harm, or existing organisms increase to a harmful level?

This question can require a significant level of technical expertise, and consultation with experts may be required. It has to be appreciated that hazards such as bacterial growth can be cumulative and thus numerous process steps need to be considered to make a judgement.

### 5. Will a subsequent process step effectively control the hazard?

This question allows for consideration that the hazard will be removed at a later stage. Thus, if cooking of raw meat is to take place later in a process, earlier stages are not critical.

Two areas of concern must be expressed at this point, however. First, remember that a later cooking stage does not address physical or most chemical hazards, and will

# The seven core principles of HACCP

not remove some heat stable bacterial toxins, such as the exotoxin produced by *Staphylococcus aureus*.

Second, just because there is an effective later stage does not mean that quality related and good practice controls can be neglected at the earlier stage. HACCP should never be used as an excuse for poor hygiene practice.

Each time a decision is reached that the hazard is not critical at this point you proceed to the next hazard and reapply the decision tree.

It is my recommendation that in small- to medium-size premises with either an individual or a small HACCP team, the question of criticality is addressed by informal discussion, with the decision tree being used for areas of confusion. In larger

premises, a simplified version of the decision tree is used; reduced to three questions, as below:

## 1. Is there a significant hazard at this point?

If there is no hazard, or no hazard deemed significant, the point is not a CCP. One must not fall into the trap of assuming that because there are controls at a process step then this is a CCP; controls may be good practice or quality related.

## 2. Is there likely to be harm caused if not addressed at this point?

Even if there is a significant hazard then it may be addressed at a later point. For instance, if there is no control at the point of delivery of a raw chicken to a catering premises, the product will still end up safe at

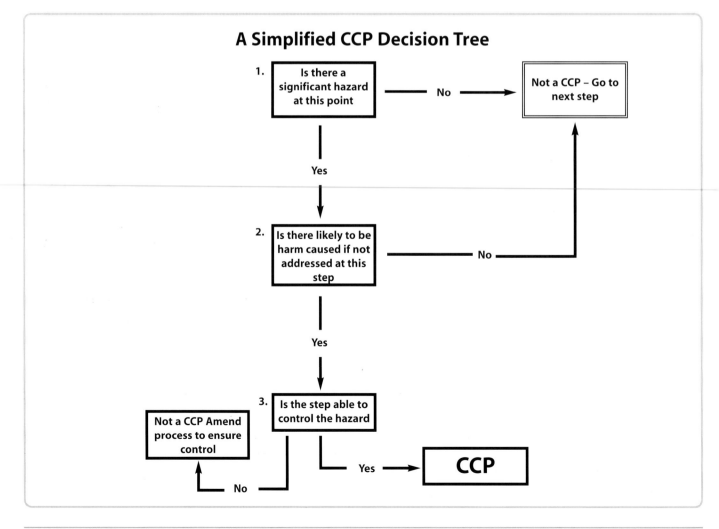

the point of consumption if it is going to be roasted at a later process step, thus delivery is not a critical control point.

### 3. Can the step control the hazard?

If the process step is incapable of controlling the hazard, then an extra or later process step must do so, thus the process will require altering. For example, concern over foreign body contamination is not addressed at a cooking step, therefore, control for this hazard must be addressed elsewhere and this would not be a CCP for this hazard.

If the answer is yes to all these points, the process step is a critical control point. This process is simpler than the five questions and is much less likely to be misinterpreted. The CCPs should now be marked on the HACCP plan, either by a separate column or a protocol highlighted on the flow diagram. This could be a different coloured box, highlighting or labelling. It is also recommended that the path through the decision tree (if utilised) is recorded on the HACCP plan in the form of a table as below.

| | Q1 | Q2 | Q3 | Q4 | Q5 | CCP y/n |
|---|---|---|---|---|---|---|
| Salad preparation | Y | Y | Y | - | - | Y |
| Salad storage | Y | Y | Y | - | - | Y |
| Heating of chilli sauce | N | - | - | - | - | N |

It is the norm with many new HACCP documents that far more process steps are included than should be. In some premises I have seen all process steps identified as critical. Whilst this can be considered better than omitting a crucial step it will result in failure of the document. Thus, steps should be re-examined by the HACCP team to consider the possibility of this zealousness and they should question whether process redesign could eliminate some of the hazards and thus CCPs, or whether the scope

of the plan needs reviewing. It is one of the criticisms of the HACCP decision tree approach that it helps us address hazards when sometimes they could be easily removed by the application of common sense and process alteration.

One way of addressing the problem of excessive and quality orientated CCPs is currently out of favour, but I have seen it used effectively in a HACCP plan that is addressing both physical and microbiological hazards. It is to use a hierarchy of CCPs. An absolute control, such as thermal processing for a microbiological hazard or sieving for physical contaminants, is labelled as a **CCP 1**. A non-absolute or limiting control, such as refrigeration for microbiological hazards or the covering of goods for physical contamination, is labelled a **CCP 2**. This has the effect of highlighting the key CCPs when there is a lot of physical hazard CCPs to cloud them. Alternatively, if the company is including quality parameters within the HACCP plan then points can be labelled as Quality Control Points (QCPs) on the plan. If either of these protocols is utilised it is imperative that all involved understand them, that they do not detract from the main CCPs and thus are included in the scope.

At this stage of the HACCP plan, it must be decided whether to list monitoring and corrective actions for non-CCPs, as they will have value in good practice or in addressing quality issues. It is my recommendation that in the core HACCP document you do not list these for non-CCPs. If you do, ensure that the CCPs are highlighted as much as possible to ensure they are not clouded by non-CCP controls.

> **HACCP TEAM BUILDING?**
> See the exercises for HACCP Team Building in EXERCISE TWO on *page 100*.

# The seven core principles of HACCP

# Revision questions

## Part three: principle two

1.    A critical control point is:

   a) The process step where the most serious hazard is identified
   b) The point where it is easiest to control a hazard
   c) A process step where lack of control will result in a threat to food safety
   d) The product that has received most customer complaints

2.    Which of the following is always true about a critical control point?

   a) Cooking is always a critical control point
   b) Control after a CCP is less important
   c) If you already monitor at a process step, it is a CCP
   d) CCPs must be monitored

# The seven core principles of HACCP

## Principle three: critical limits

At this stage we have identified all the hazards in the operation and highlighted those hazards that must be controlled for the purpose of food safety. The rest of the HACCP plan is effectively to ensure the efficiency of these targeted controls, and is thus specific to the critical control points. Each of the next stages of the plan is related and follows on logically from CCP identification.

The next stage is to identify the critical limit for each of the CCPs. A critical limit is the monitorable limit which if exceeded means the CCP will not be effective, and thus the identified hazard may be realised (an out-of-control situation). The limit set must obviously relate directly to the hazard identified; thus limits can relate to physical, chemical or microbiological hazards. Decisions on what constitutes a harmful level require technical food safety knowledge, but in smaller premises the limits usually reflect the current legal requirement.

Critical limits must also as far as possible be exact and monitorable. Statements like 'good personal hygiene' or 'effective cleaning' are open to interpretation and variable, and thus easy to pass off as being complied with. Similarly, it is difficult to set a bacterial level such as three day TVC (total viable count) because by the time the result is achieved, the product has exceeded its 'use-by' date. Good examples would include processing or storage temperatures, presence of foreign materials, ATP limits, time limits and, increasingly with rapid diagnostic methods, presence of pathogens.

The evident problem with establishing just a critical limit is that should monitoring illustrate that the limit has been exceeded, the product is out of control and likely to have to be destroyed. Thus in most systems,

it is advisable to build in a hierarchy of action levels and associated actions, possibly by establishing a target level, with or without acceptable tolerances, or by having a first level action limit and a critical limit.

A good illustration of this is refrigeration temperatures. If we establish the critical limit as being the current UK legal standard (8°C in excess of four hours for product temperature), then in any situation that this is exceeded for high-risk foodstuffs the product requires a corrective action, such as product disposal. Therefore the critical limit is 8°C and four hours. This is obviously expensive and reactive, and runs the risks of products being missed by monitoring, and of introducing hazards during monitoring. It is advisable, therefore, to set an action level that is better than the legal requirement (and certainly should never be worse than the legally required minimum!). We can monitor air temperature (or a 'plastic sausage' food temperature equivalent) as an indicator and set a number of action levels; for example 5°C (air temperature) exceeded initiates an increased monitoring frequency and 8°C (air temperature) initiates product temperature assessment and removal of products below 8°C to an alternative refrigerator, pending investigation by a refrigeration engineer. In such a situation the monitoring frequency is important as it has to show how long the product has been out of control.

This then enables us to take relevant action before the product goes 'out of control'. Alternatively, we can establish a target of 4°C and a tolerance of +/–4°C. This type of limit is useful when variance up or down results in non-conformance.

It is imperative that if a variety of action levels are used that the critical limit, above which non-conformance is identified, is highlighted. If there is a variety of actions at different levels then it is advisable to make use of recorded standard operating procedures to identify the action to be taken.

It must be remembered that whether based on scientific knowledge or legislation, critical limits are always the subject of review.

At this juncture it is worth spending some time checking that the established critical limits are reflected in and do not conflict with existing documentation and procedures. It is useless recording this level if staff are still checking to another level, and existing training materials do not reflect the new critical limit.

---

**HACCP TEAM BUILDING?**
See the exercises for HACCP Team Building in EXERCISE TWO on *page 100*.

---

# Principle four: monitoring critical limits

The logical progression and link between these central principles is obvious; having established what levels are necessary at critical points to ensure food safety it follows that we now have to develop and implement a monitoring regime (at the CCPs) to ensure that the control is effective. This monitoring must be able to ensure that products exceeding critical limit are not dispatched and able to realise their hazard; the monitoring must keep the product under control. The nature (depth) and frequency (extent or width) of the monitoring will therefore be variable, depending on the production method and the nature of the hazard.

The consideration of depth is that the monitoring must be thorough enough to assess the compliance with the critical limit. It should therefore directly assess the parameter in which the critical limit is established and it should be at the critical

control point in the process or as soon after as is possible. In some situations assessment of another indicator is possible, although there should be strong scientific evidence of the link, and generally speaking this should only be done for first tier action levels, not critical limits. Monitoring that is rapid and 'on line' is the ideal in most situations, as 'off line' assessment (such as the taking of samples to assess mycotoxin levels) is likely to take longer and be less representative.

The consideration of frequency is directly related to the extent of control that can be exerted over the product. If batches of a product are produced across a whole day and able to be held safely, without deterioration, the sampling frequency can be daily. This might be the case on the production of canned goods undergoing assessment for viable thermophilic spoilage organisms. If products deteriorate rapidly if out of control, they need to be monitored frequently and, ideally, constantly. This is the case when high-risk foodstuffs are held refrigerated. If there is a frequency, consideration must be made to products that might need disposing of since the last monitoring, thus the cost of the product relative to the cost of monitoring also has a bearing on the establishment of the frequency. If the monitoring is not constant, there should be formal record of the required frequency; statements such as 'regularly' are obviously inadequate.

Having established the nature and frequency of monitoring, it is now necessary to formalise as far as practicable the methodology of monitoring. The monitoring of a cooked chicken, for example, can vary greatly dependent upon the exact spot of probe insertion; so the method used must be as uniform as it can be made. Use of a recorded methodology or ideally a SOP (standard operating procedure; see section, 'some post-HACCP principles') should be considered. This provides uniformity and also offers an ideal medium for training.

# The seven core principles of HACCP

Consideration should also be made as to who is to carry out the monitoring and how this is to be checked. Base level monitoring is notoriously difficult to control as the staff involved may lack motivation or training. The competency of the individual is obviously linked to training, and the part of the food safety policy regarding allocation of responsibility. Incorporation of CCP monitoring into management checks is thus required, as detailed in the section, 'HACCP and food safety management'.

The final consideration in relation to monitoring is the means of recording. Not only is documentation a principle of HACCP (and indeed of Quality Assurance), but also the monitoring serves as an essential aspect of a 'due diligence' defence. To this end it is recommended that the monitoring column of the HACCP plan makes reference to a monitoring form.

In some circumstances a record of the above points is made on the HACCP plan to illustrate they have been considered by the HACCP team.

There should also be clearly indicated on any documentation or training materials the required corrective action to be taken if the monitoring exceeds the indicated critical limit; and this takes us to the next principle of HACCP.

> **HACCP TEAM BUILDING?**
> See the exercises for HACCP Team Building in EXERCISE TWO on *page 100*.

# Principle five: corrective action

Having carried out monitoring to make an assessment as to whether or not a critical limit has been exceeded, it follows that we now need to detail what action to take in this 'out-of-control' situation. There may be two levels of limits to be monitored (a first and second action level) and thus two (or sometimes more) actions to be undertaken, but the crucial thing on which to concentrate is the action that is necessary to stop any hazard being realised. It can often seem that corrective actions are common sense and need no written statement but unless they are listed as a positive action and unambiguous, it is likely that they will be ignored or abused.

Assuming that a critical limit has been exceeded, there are two major considerations of the corrective action; cause specific and product specific. For example, if a refrigerator is operating at 18°C because the motor blows, we need to take action to rectify the fault (call a refrigerator engineer), but we also need to take action to deal with the product (disposal of all high risk-products in this case). Remember that the corrective action must address the hazard, and product disposal is not the only action; it is sometimes possible to reprocess or rework the product.

If the action to be taken is due to deviation from a target, the action can be cause-related or involve product alteration (examples would include alteration of equipment settings, or addition of extra ingredients to the product). It need not involve product disposal.

In some situations (presence of foreign bodies, for example) it is difficult to specify a particular corrective action and this is subject to some form of assessment. This might be a more detailed (usually off-line) assessment or increased sampling. Or it might involve human assessment, and this is the sort of situation where a written record is needed (see 'Impact analysis' under the Post-HACCP principles section). Consideration must be given when describing a corrective action as to who is empowered to carry out the corrective action; and this should be described under the responsibilities section of the food safety policy.

# The seven core principles of HACCP

As discussed previously many corrective actions will be repetitive procedures and it makes sense to record these as standard operating procedures. In line with principles of Quality Control the action taken should be recorded. Consideration of using Corrective Action Request forms (see example below) should be considered. Not only does this ensure that the action to be taken is easy to understand but it allows it to be written off, and provides a record that ensures that recurring faults can be picked up.

This provides the end of the logical progression of the core principles of HACCP and it is worth taking time at this juncture to review the example HACCP plan that records this information in the appendices.

| CORRECTIVE ACTION REQUEST | DOCUMENT REFERENCE |
|---|---|
| **DATE OF AUDIT:** | **AUDITORS:** |

**PROCESS STEP:**

**DOCUMENT REFERENCE:**

**DETAILS OF NON CONFORMANCE:**

| REQUESTED ACTIONS | ACTION PRIORITY LEVEL | COMPLETED DATE | SIGNED |
|---|---|---|---|
|  |  |  |  |
|  |  |  |  |
|  |  |  |  |
|  |  |  |  |
|  |  |  |  |
|  |  |  |  |

Signature of Auditor:

Signature of Auditees:

# Revision questions

## Part four: principles three to five

1.    A critical limit is:

a)  The level which if exceeded results in corrective action
b)  The limit which you aim to achieve
c)  The best practice level
d)  The level which if exceeded results in review of the HACCP

2.    Under principle four monitoring should be:

a)  Undertaken for all process steps
b)  Always taken four times a day for fridge temperatures
c)  Specific to the critical limit
d)  Always done by a supervisor

3.    Which of the following is the most important example of a corrective action?

a)  Making adjustments to monitoring procedures
b)  Disposing of high-risk products that have exceeded critical temperature limits for storage
c)  Reheating high-risk products that have exceeded critical temperature limits for storage
d)  Calling out a maintenance engineer when a piece of equipment fails

4.    Why should the core information of these principles be completed in a HACCP plan?

a)  Because it is expected by enforcement officers
b)  Because it allows all key actions to be described logically
c)  Because CODEX prescribes it in principle seven
d)  Because it is required by legislation

5.    The correct order of principles three to five is:

a)  Critical limits, corrective action, monitoring
b)  Critical limits, monitoring, corrective action
c)  Critical control points, monitoring, corrective action
d)  Corrective action, critical limits, monitoring

6.    If a refrigerator is found to be at 10°C air temperature and contains high-risk foods, which of the following would be the best corrective action?

a)  Dispose of all high-risk products
b)  Alter the refrigerator setting
c)  Call out a refrigerator engineer
d)  Check product temperature, if less than 5°C increase monitoring frequency. If above 5°C transfer to alternative unit. Dispose of product only if over 8°C for four hours

# The seven core principles of HACCP

HACCP provides is effective. Alternatively it might involve auditing the HACCP system to provide a measure of its effectiveness.

**Review,** whilst inextricably linked to the above, is usually taken to mean the setting of dates and a formal procedure to verify and validate the HACCP system, for example, every six months. There are also numerous situations under which review should be triggered prior to a review date.

Let us examine what practically this means we have to do to illustrate legal compliance.

It will be seen that in undertaking the development of the HACCP plan in this manual there are identified milestones. These should be seen as steps at which verification and validation of each step is made, for example, confirming that the flow diagram really reflects the process.

The HACCP document is produced at a point in time, at the conclusion of the HACCP process. It is hoped that the level of control exerted by the HACCP system will ensure conformance and product safety. There is, however, a possibility that there will be variations in the process over time; due to contract changes, seasonal variations, changes in specifications or equipment, etc. There is also the very real risk of the hazard altering, for example, as emergent pathogens occur, or scientific knowledge of the harmful levels of mycotoxins changes. It is therefore possible that any variation will result in the realisation of a hazard, and thus any variations in the process require adjustment of the control parameters. There is a direct relation between the ability to validate a system and the level of scientific knowledge, and thus the constant training of key HACCP team members is necessary, as is the seeking of advice from experts in the particular field.

Whilst end-product sampling is not a necessary step in HACCP, it is usual to employ some means of sampling of the end product as a means of validating the system, and this forms a part of the validation process and thus should be recorded and incorporated in the HACCP plan. If parameters of sampling are exceeded this should trigger investigation, formal review, and in some situations crisis management procedures. The company should consider these limits and set them down as part of verification and validation. Customer complaints may also indicate that such action is necessary; see section, 'Some post HACCP principles.'

Review programmes should be formalised as the HACCP programme is completed; with most premises an absolute maximum period of six months is required, although it is usual to convene the HACCP team more frequently to conduct review of the HACCP. If amendments are made it is important that document control procedures are used to control the out-of-date documents.

There is also a number of situations when HACCP review should be brought forward, these include the following:

## New product line

A new product line will require production of a new product specific HACCP plan, or amendment of a process led plan to incorporate any variations. HACCP should be considered as a principle in product development, as it can be used to help design a safe production process. All too often HACCP is added after the product has been produced for six months; the wrong way round.

## Process amendment

If a process is changed, the HACCP plan does not reflect the way in which the product is produced. This will therefore require amendment to the HACCP process flow diagram and reassessment of hazards. Situations when this is necessary may be new equipment, a new form or specification of raw product, change in premises layout and therefore product flow, or process alteration at client request.

## Product amendment

In some situations the end product may vary but not the process. Reassessment of hazards is thus required on the basis of this new information. Normally, this is a result of client request. Examples would include alteration to period of minimum durability, alteration of end user to be an at-risk group, alteration to end user processing instructions or storage instructions

## Significant alteration of good hygiene practice

As the assessment of hazards is undertaken on the status of GHP it is necessary to re-evaluate hazards if they change significantly. For example, if a new building is used, a new cleaning regime is established or alterations are made to the means of hand washing.

## Change in scientific knowledge of hazards

Even if nothing within the premises alters, sometimes external factors change, either with the advancement of science or with the identification of a new pathogen. The advent of VTEC, for example, has greatly increased the hazards from comminuted beef products and led to a reconsideration of their safety. New legal limits of acceptable levels of certain toxins (such as mycotoxins) may also require review.

## Routine monitoring, audit outcomes or customer complaints illustrates system failure

All the aspects of verification and validation so far discussed can illustrate that something has gone wrong and these parameters should trigger a full HACCP review.

The HACCP team should monitor the above constantly as very often something will trigger review before the formal review date. Ideally, review should reassess all stages of the HACCP principles.

All changes to a HACCP plan or related documents must be well managed; documents should be altered and approved, old documents removed and replaced, the live document clearly labelled, and any procedural changes relayed to relevant staff who should be retrained if necessary.

In addition to the internal review, consideration should be given to the use of some external validation, as the HACCP team can find it difficult to look objectively at a plan in which they have been so involved. There are numerous companies acting in a consultancy role that will carry out third party independent audits of a HACCP system at a cost. Furthermore, enforcement officers should make an assessment of the system during enforcement audits.

However, much can be done within one organisation, particularly if the company has a number of sites. Using HACCP team members or hygiene specialists from an alternative site provides a fresh perspective and is a recommended part of the verification process. Trade organisations or federations can often play a similar role. Persons carrying out such a role are referred to in the section, 'Auditing HACCP systems'.

# The seven core principles of HACCP

## Principle seven: documentation

HACCP documentation is often one of its problems; the extent of paperwork generated serves to cloud the necessary actions. It is worth, therefore, returning to basics as to why documentation is necessary.

The key purposes of HACCP documentation are to ensure product safety and to illustrate that all seven principles have been followed. Despite the lack of current requirements for documentation in horizontal legislation, there are evident advantages, as previously mentioned. Documentation serves to illustrate legal compliance to the other principles, it makes review easier, it provides a marketing advantage and it serves to contribute to 'due diligence', either in court or to an enforcement officer. However, these

advantages will be more valid if the documentation provided is concise, easy to follow and not too long. To this end let us review the previous principles and highlight the nature of HACCP documentation required to illustrate their completion. Then we shall proceed to list associated documentation that is needed to support the HACCP. The following diagram is designed to illustrate this.

**Principle one.** The earlier elements of principle one are illustrated in the initial sheet of the HACCP plan; often referred to as the scope or terms of reference (although it normally contains much more than this). Expectations as to what is seen as necessary can be illustrated by examining the HACCP plans included in the appendices. Product description and intended use, the nature of the HACCP, HACCP team members, starting and finishing points and relation to other HACCP plans, date and review date and

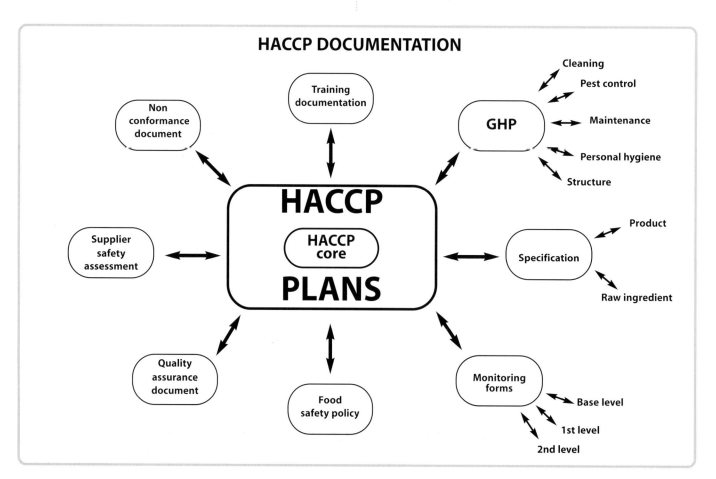

# The seven core principles of HACCP

criteria for hazard identification are normally included here. The scope will have related documentation; such as HACCP team minutes, product specifications, etc. and this should be referenced but not included within the HACCP plan.

The process analysis is then represented diagrammatically on the process flow diagram.

The latter part of Principle one, hazard identification, is usually the first stage of the HACCP chart.

**Principles two to five.** All the core stages are then represented on the rest of the HACCP chart. The CCPs are normally also represented on the process flow diagram. Monitoring will be supported by the documentation generated by monitoring forms. Examples should be included in the HACCP plan but used documentation stored separately.

**Principle six.** Review dates should be indicated on the scope and a description of situations for review made in the HACCP core.

In conclusion, documentation of a HACCP system is usually made up of a number of elements.

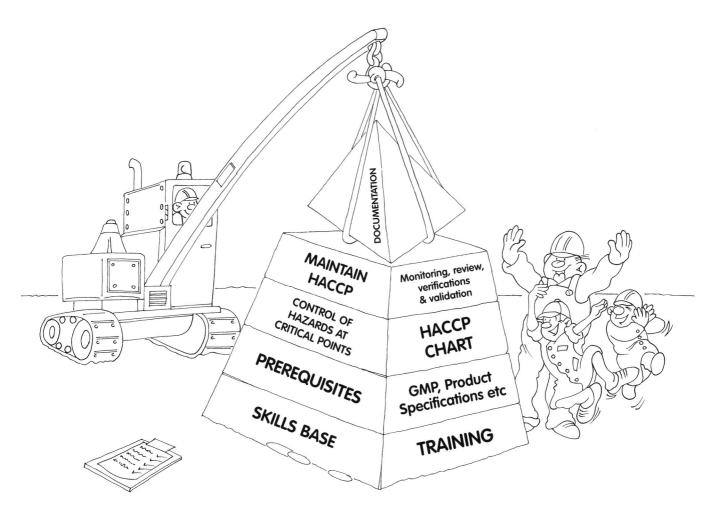

## Building an effective HACCP: 5 documentation

# The seven core principles of HACCP

The HACCP document consists of:

**HACCP core.** This is an overview of the whole and should explain the relationship of the HACCP to other systems.

**HACCP terms of reference/scope.** There is a scope for each product/process and it provides product or process specific details.

**HACCP process flow diagram.** This represents the process.

**HACCP chart.** This illustrates the main principles. It may be split to provide a separate hazard identification chart, and/or a separate CCP control plan.

Other documentation is then closely referenced and acts as a support or outcome of the HACCP. Examples are shown on the above diagram and can be found referred to in relevant sections of the manual.

## EXAMPLE HACCP CHART

| PRODUCT: | | | | DATE FINALISED:<br>DOC REFERENCE NUMBER: | | DATE FINISHED: | |
|---|---|---|---|---|---|---|---|
| STEP | HAZARDS | SIGNIFICANT Y/N? | CCP Y/N? | CRITICAL LIMIT | MONITORING | CORRECTIVE ACTION | DOCUMENTATION |
| | | | | | | | |

# Revision questions

## Part five: principles six and seven

1.       **Which of the following is a situation that should always result in review of a HACCP system?**

    a)  **Inspection by an enforcement officer**
    b)  **A customer complaint**
    c)  **Alteration to a process**
    d)  **Poor raw product sample results**

2.       **Which of the following is true about documentation?**

    a)  **It is a legal requirement in all premises**
    b)  **It is an unnecessary waste of time**
    c)  **It should always conform with ISO 9000 principles**
    d)  **It serves as a good training tool**

3.       **Which of the following do NOT play a part in verification?**

    a)  **External validation**
    b)  **Routine sampling**
    c)  **Calibration of monitoring equipment**
    d)  **Regular HACCP team meetings**

# Some post-HACCP principles

soon arrives that there is no end point. HACCP should at this juncture be integral to the way food safety is controlled. We also begin to appreciate that with the flexible nature of most of the food industry, the process of review is also never ending.

However, having produced, implemented and incorporated HACCP and established review procedures, there are a few things we should do at this stage. Shamelessly most of these involve patting people on the back:

- Gratitude should formally be given to the HACCP team, and in particular the HACCP co-ordinator, who quite probably will need a holiday at this point.

- Incorporation of the status of HACCP in marketing materials, and dissemination of its role to marketing staff.

- If not already done, the information produced during the baseline audit should be reviewed to illustrate the benefits the system has endowed on the process.

- Ensure all training courses and training materials fully reflect the role HACCP plays in food safety.

Although this marks a closing point in the HACCP process there is also an additional section to serve as an introduction to the auditing of HACCP systems. The reader is also directed to the case studies and related questions (Exercises one and two), which should serve to help apply knowledge up to this point.

# Auditing HACCP systems

Auditing is effectively in-depth inspection against a known standard. The word has many connotations with regard to the external validation of Quality Control systems and some of these protocols are incorporated here. A HACCP audit is, however, somewhat different in that as well as being against a written standard, it requires technical assessment and much more visual inspection, for we are also examining compliance with current knowledge of safety.

It is common that anyone involved in HACCP will at some juncture be involved in the auditing of a HACCP system; this might be for the purpose of internal verification **(first party audit)**, to audit suppliers **(second party audit)**, to carry out external audits for the purpose of some type of consultancy or external validation **(third party audit)** or for enforcement purposes **(fourth party audit)**. Auditing thus becomes one of the primary means of the validation of a HACCP system, as per principle six. Knowledge of HACCP is evidently required, but the approach is different from that of someone establishing a system within their own organisation. This section is aimed to serve as an introduction to those who have to carry out this task. It, therefore, introduces concepts of auditing but does not have the scope of fully covering auditing skills or Quality Control auditing principles. One should not be confused here by the use of the term quality; referring to consistency, and organoleptic product quality.

Put simply, auditing is a detailed inspection against a specific standard. The specific standard in this instance is usually the company's HACCP document, although other standards, such as legislation or company/industry procedures may be the basis for auditing. The decision as to what is the agreed standard is the beginning of carrying out the audit. The audit then becomes the systematic examination, evaluation and, finally, reporting on objective evidence found as to the compliance or non-compliance with the given standard.

The HACCP auditor often finds they have two tasks: auditing to find non-compliance with the HACCP manual; and offering technical advice on failings in the standard. The role of the HACCP auditor generally extends beyond the role of Quality Control auditor, who has no role in rectifying the deficiency. Similarly, the HACCP auditor will have to incorporate compliance to general hygiene practice that may not be written, and product/process knowledge, into the visual inspection component of the audit.

The audit is normally of the HACCP system and related procedures, and as the system is based upon the control of the production process, the audit is referred to as a **horizontal audit.** We are interested in the process, and anything that contributes to product safety, not the role of departments or sections.

Auditing of HACCP systems is a time-consuming and difficult task. The skills needed are multitudinous; the auditor requires a detailed understanding of HACCP and significant knowledge of the products being audited, such as common ingredients, common processes, hazards and controls. Detailed food safety technical knowledge is required for the assessment of hazards or of the efficiency of controls. Also needed are skills that are required by any auditor, the ability to manage the audit, to question and examine, to receive information, to assimilate and reach conclusions, and to be able to communicate these findings in both written and verbal forms.

Such skills are difficult to achieve and the auditor is constantly learning. Whatever the skills of the individual, it is a time-consuming business. It is ludicrous that supplier auditors or enforcement officers can claim to effectively audit a HACCP system of a medium to large manufacturing company

# Auditing HACCP systems

should be minuted. The exact detail of this meeting will depend on the size of the company and the nature of the audit, but key areas to include are:

- introduction of staff members
- previous audit outcomes
- the nature of the audit
- timetable, including tentative arrangements for the closing meeting
- requirements regarding access
- requirements regarding office and equipment provision.

It may at times be necessary to explain that the audit will require expanding beyond the HACCP document to associated documentation and good hygiene practice.

Particularly with third and fourth party audits (especially enforcement based) communication is difficult. Once aware of this, one can make it an aim of the briefing meeting to engender an element of trust and communication at the outset. The auditor should be open about what they are looking for and what the outcomes might be. Ensure that positive aspects are presented as well as failures.

## b) Collection of objective evidence

The key tools of the HACCP auditor are visual examination of documentation, inspection and questioning/listening. All are difficult skills.

### Documentation examination and questioning

The initial stages of the audit will be office based, using a checklist the auditor will normally progress in the order of HACCP principles, checking relevant documentation. References to separate documents or procedures should be noted on the checklist and followed up later. To fully understand a HACCP document requires a thorough understanding of its history, including timescales and key roles of team members, and if not previously ascertained this is a good starting point for the questioning of documentation. This will naturally progress onto the next stages of development proposed, and form a good understanding of the current status of the HACCP system.

Most HACCP documents are verbose and difficult to follow; they must be stripped to their bones to be understood. This can only be done by a combination of examination of documentation, practical inspection and questioning. It has to be recognised that it is not practicable to examine every piece of paper and every event in process manufacture. The key questions we are trying to answer are: Is every product and process covered? Are all seven HACCP principles addressed? Are required standards complied with? Is product safety ensured? Despite anything else these are the key concerns and examination should continue until they can be addressed. The primary aim in document examination is to ensure that all seven principles of HACCP have been covered and that all products are dealt with. It will also enable the auditor to become aware of essential elements of process control and testing that can be practically verified later. At the same time, document control should also be examined. The HACCP document should be dated and be marked as 'live', and will often be the subject of numbering for this purpose.

As you progress through the core documentation, try not to be distracted by peripheral but related documentation, such as specifications, training records and GMP but make a note of them as you progress and check them later. The format of a checklist is seen as essential in managing the audit in this fashion.

The document examination will highlight key areas of safety, and these main control points should be verified by inspection and questioning. All of these should be the subject of monitoring documentation and this should also be examined. Questioning will often be of the 'what if?' type as you explore how the system deals with various atypical situations. Try and question a cross-section of responsible staff, as the HACCP co-ordinator will probably have all the right answers off to a fine art. Do not be afraid to try key control systems by some sort of practical examination, such as passing test metal samples through a metal detector. Inspection should also be made of any written good manufacturing practice documents on which the HACCP is based, and these should be verified during the inspection.

## Visual inspection/examination

Ideally, practical inspection should be of the downstream type, that is, it starts with raw ingredients and progresses through the production process to the use/dispatch or sale of the final product. Not only does this fit in with the flow diagram, and allows you to verify this, it also ensures no stage of the process is omitted.

In conducting a downstream inspection the auditor is examining three principle areas:

people and the movement of people; product and the movement of the product; and structure and equipment. I would recommend that in learning to audit, the path be followed three times to learn these skills, but even in the experienced inspector all three strands should be considered.

## Questioning/listening

Given that the auditor is only present for a snapshot of time of the process operation much assessment has to be made by a process of questioning and listening. If the auditor is not welcomed or the auditee is auditor-weary, this can be a difficult process.

It will help greatly if the questions are easy to understand, well presented and structured to be linked and progress logically. The structure of the checklist format will aid this.

The nature of the questions is also important; they should be structured to enable the auditee to answer fully and present all the necessary information. Open questions and linked questions are, therefore, useful. Let us assume we need to examine that incoming ingredient specifications are well documented. The question 'Do you have a written raw product specification?' will illicit the response 'Yes', but you are not able to provide objective evidence of compliance or otherwise from this response. The following question links are an example of open questioning that will test and allow the effective verification of this requirement.

Any situation that is not consistent with the seven principles of HACCP, or that is seen as compromising product safety, should be

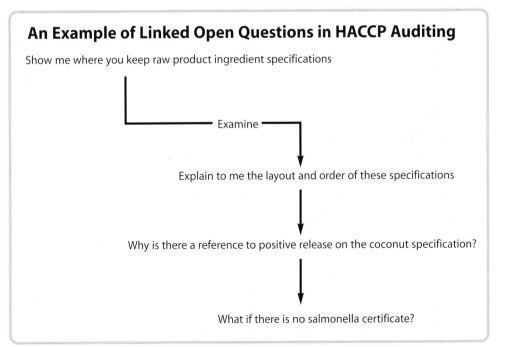

**An Example of Linked Open Questions in HACCP Auditing**

Show me where you keep raw product ingredient specifications

Examine

Explain to me the layout and order of these specifications

Why is there a reference to positive release on the coconut specification?

What if there is no salmonella certificate?

highlighted as a major non-conformance. Other variations to any standard that do not affect product safety should be marked as minor non-conformance. Any areas for improvement should be listed as observations or recommendations. If a proper assessment of a situation cannot be made at the time of the audit (due to no production, equipment failure, missing documentation, etc.) it is important that this is also listed otherwise it will be assumed to be correct. As far as is practicable, full reasoning should be given that a non-conformance has been identified, with reference to documentation. The listed non-conformance form the basis of the outcome of the audit and of the closing meeting.

It is usual to take time to consolidate the information in private prior to the closing meeting. This will allow you to gather your thoughts, examine any documentation, even contact other parties before you reach a conclusion. Do not be bullied into the closing meeting.

### c) Closing meeting

The purpose of the meeting is to convey the main points of the findings of the audit. For this reason the meeting, as the opening meeting, should be recorded, attendance noted and key points minuted.

Normally all non-conformance are discussed, and if applicable a decision on suggested action is also highlighted. This will obviously depend on the nature of the audit, and may be approval or otherwise for a contract, enforcement action or internal request for action.

In a formal audit situation each non-conformance highlighted becomes the basis of a corrective action request (CAR) (See example on *page 70*). Whether or not this protocol is followed, it must be made clear not only what was wrong, but also the extent of action expected. You should not, however, be totally prescriptive in what action is required, although be prepared to

be asked your opinion on a variety of matters. It is normal in auditing to ask for a response to the audit report within ten working days. If you expect action within a specified period this should obviously be disclosed and recorded on the audit report.

Following discussions of these points, the summary document should be signed by both parties and forms the basis of the audit report.

### Quantifying audit results

If you are required to make repeat visits to a HACCP system, or required to make comparison between different systems, it is often advantageous to provide some means of quantifying the audit output. A checklist can be constructed to do this, providing points for effective prerequisites and certain standards. Percentage deductions can then be made for major non-conformance, for example, to provide weighting. If such a scoring system is used in a team of HACCP auditors, consistency in use needs to be ensured by trial audits and exercises.

The detail of formal ISO auditor training is not always necessary for those carrying out HACCP auditing, but it does provide valuable lessons and skills. The above is based on the adaptation of these formal skills to real situations and should not be seen as, for example, an ISO 9000 audit. It is hoped it provides some insight and a starting point for those who have to audit, and indeed for those being audited.

# Concluding statements

I never said it was going to be easy, but let us hope it was easier than it otherwise might have been. Most importantly, I hope it contributes to what a HACCP system is supposed to achieve, i.e. the production of safe food.

When you are bogged down on the long journey to the perfect HACCP system, it is worth focusing on the following words of advice:

1. *'Our primary aim is the production of safe food. Whatever other aims you have in pleasing large customers or the enforcement officer, remain focused on this.'*

2. *'We are all still learning. Let us accept that and learn together.'*

3. *'Do as much as is necessary, not as much as is possible.'*

Thank you for your time, and the best of luck... The following pages contain a lot of information that you will find useful: two exercises, a glossary of technical words; answers to the revision questions and a list of the references you will find in the manual.

# Auditing HACCP systems

## Add your notes here

| ACTION POINT | PAGE | COMMENT |
|---|---|---|
| | | |

# Exercise one

## Examination of an existing HACCP plan

The following is part of a HACCP plan for a supermarket chain. The exercise is split into parts progressing through the stages of HACCP. At each stage you are asked to examine the limited documentation given and make suggestions for improvement. It is intended to be a realistic (but poor) attempt at a HACCP plan.

Those involved are asked to answer in the context of the size (chain of 12 premises) and the nature (variable delicatessen products) of the example given.

The exercise can be used at the end of reading the text as a means of consolidating knowledge gained. Alternatively, it can be used as a training aid at the end of each learning outcome of the HACCP principles.

The answers given are not detailed or exhaustive but are intended to provide some guidance and structure for either those checking their own knowledge or for group discussion.

### Question

*Examine the preceding front sheet and following single process scope for a supermarket chain delicatessen counter. There are 12 premises. Remembering the type of premises and the nature of the product, suggest areas for improvement.*

### Answer(front sheet)

The main problem with this plan relates, to the use of a generic plan to cover a number of premises.

Presuming that all 12 stores have a delicatessen counter (and we don't know how many ) there is probably a variation in the structure, products and processes used, and questions have to be asked about how such variations are or are not addressed.

How the document is communicated to managers and to staff is inadequate from what we are told and the issue of training and responsibility is not defined.

There is also concern over the HACCP covering such a broad range of products. The phrasing could cover just about any product, and a number of different processes. These include in-house cooked products. A list of products should have been provided, as it is not clear what 'approved cooked meat products' are. There is also confusion over the issue of any salads prepared on site as this is not covered but not precluded. The final statement of 'other speciality products' is again ill defined and was included to cover some seasonal products and products such as roll-mop herrings which the team were uncertain about.

---

**HACCP for DELICATESSEN COUNTERS SUPADUPA MARKETS**

This HACCP plan is for all stores who have a delicatessen counter within the Supadupa market group. It includes sale of approved cooked meat products, in-house cooked products and pre-prepared salad products and other speciality products.

The HACCP team that produced the plan was Frank Flowers (Group Hygiene Officer) and Harold Pintail (Regional Manager Region West).

The document was finalised on 23rd January 1999 and sent to all managers in May 2000. It is the managers' responsibility to ensure that relevant staff are made aware of their responsibilities.

All monitoring forms referred to in this document are to be found in the 'HYGIENE MONITORING SHEETS' folder held by the manager at each site.

It is intended to review the HACCP document every 12 months.

# Exercise two

## HACCP team building

The following exercise is designed to be used by a HACCP team as a means of the team working together through progressive stages of the HACCP process. It is structured as the material to be given to the HACCP team within the box, with some discussion on the outcome of the exercise below for the benefit of the facilitator (probably the HACCP co-ordinator).

You will find within the body of the text in the manual a box showing the suggested point at which the exercise should be carried out; but for ease of use these are also summarised below.

There is plenty of scope for these exercises to be adopted for the needs of a particular company.

Please note that this type of exercise is to promote discussion, to allow agreement on an area to be vocalised. As such there is no right or wrong answer.

## Exercise two
### part 1 - approaching the HACCP plan

> Ask the HACCP team members to write, in two minutes, as many answers as they can give to the following question:
>
> **What is HACCP?**

**Outcome/discussion**

The contributions made should be used as the basis of a discussion, allowing each member in turn to present their answer. Be positive in your response, but ask the opinion of other team members to a given answer.

The exercise serves to give an indication of the previous knowledge and understanding of the HACCP team. The exercise might serve to indicate any resistance to the scheme, and thus identify difficult team members. It can also raise certain misconcepts ('it's a way of ensuring quality').

In some situations the team might give the answer 'hazard analysis and critical control points' which requires a supplementary question.

## Exercise two
### part 2 - step one: the HACCP team

> Ask the HACCP team members to individually fill in the following:
>
> **What can you contribute to this HACCP team?**

**Outcome/discussion**

Allow each member to present their answer to the others.

In addition to Exercise one this allows each individual member to identify the skills they have. Do not allow the discussion

# Exercise two

to be a competition. Highlight the breadth and type of skills needed and how they are all equally valuable.

## Exercise two
## part 3 - step four: the process flow diagram

Select one of your products of which as many people as possible will have knowledge (but ideally of which no one person has exhaustive knowledge). Provide written product details if necessary. In groups of two (or more if more than six members) ask the team to do the following:

*List all the process steps and show them in the form of a flow diagram.*

### Outcome/discussion
Allow each group to present their flow diagram (ideally, on a board or flip chart) and allow brief discussion.

The exercise illustrates the variances of flow diagrams and forms the starting point on reaching agreement on the type of diagram to be used and an ideal number of steps to reflect the complexity of the product.

## Exercise two
## part 4 - step five: The identification of hazards

Allow individuals ten minutes to complete the following as if it were part of a HACCP plan.

**HAZARD**          **CONTROL MEASURE**

Microbial growth
*(in storage of cooked meat)*

Glass contamination
*(in filling of bottled pickles)*

Salmonella in incoming
raw eggs *(receipt of raw*

*ingredients to a bakery)*
Microbial survival
*(cooking step of a
catering operation)*

### Outcome/discussion
Collect in the answers and then read out any differences.

This provides a discussion forum for the type of wording for hazards and how specific the wording need be. It also points out the need for hazard specific controls, and that there can be more than one control for a given hazard.

## Exercise two
## part 5 - principle two: Critical control points

Break the group into groups of two (or more if there are more than six team members). Provide the groups with the CODEX CCP decision tree *(see page 62)*, or the simplified version if you intend to use this later. For each of the given process steps listed ask the members to progress through the decision tree, recording their answers. You may be able to replace the following answers with process steps from a known process.

1. **Sieving of incoming flour into a bread-baking process.**
2. **Metal detection of meat pies prior to packing and refrigerated dispatch.**
3. **Cooking of a meat-based casserole prior to hot hold display.**
4. **Reheating of a cook-chill meal at a satellite kitchen on a hospital ward.**

### Outcome/discussion
Ask each group to present their answer for one of the given examples, and see if other groups agree with both the outcome and the path through the decision tree.

This serves to provide a medium for

# Exercise two

discussion of the role and difficulties of the decision tree, and provide some uniformity in its use.

N.B. - Keep the answers from this exercise as they may be useful in the next exercise which uses the same process steps.

## Exercise two
## Part 6 - principle three: Critical limits

Using the same examples as the previous exercise it will be noted that each of the identified steps has a control element. On the assumption they were identified as CCPs, ask the groups of two to identify logical critical limits.

| CONTROL | CRITICAL LIMITS |
|---|---|
| 1. Sieving of incoming flour into a bread-baking process. | |
| 2. Metal detection of meat pies prior to packing and refrigerated dispatch. | |
| 3. Cooking of a meat-based casserole prior to hot hold display. | |
| 4. Reheating of a cook-chill meal at a satellite kitchen on a hospital ward. | |

### Outcome/discussion

Collect the given answers and identify any differences highlighted.

This forms the basis for discussion on the nature of critical limits, targets, tolerances, etc and allows for a protocol to be agreed. Discuss any limits that are not exact or not monitorable and highlight the difficulty

these cause.

## Exercise two
## Part 7 - principle five: Corrective action

In small groups ask the team to answer the following. Allow about ten minutes.

**For each of the given critical limits describe a logical action if the limit is found to be exceeded.**

Product temperature of 8°C for high-risk sandwiches on display.

Presence of a piece of wood in a batch of gelatin-based sweets.

Exceeded aflatoxin level in a consignment of dried fruit notified to a bakery.

### Outcome/discussion

Allow the groups to present their answers. Add complications such as: (1) the products is for immediate consumption, (2) the wood is very small or very sharp, (3) there is no other fruit available in the bakery. See if responses change.

This provides the material for discussion on the nature of corrective actions, the ease and time in monitoring, issues about who or how the monitoring should be carried out (how did the groups intend to convey this information?), how the limits should be clear (any confusion with targets, for example) and also the nature of product and cause of specific outcomes.

# HACCP 'jargon busting' glossary

## Introduction

HACCP principles are now the daily conversation in most food manufacturing premises, and amongst most food safety officers, enforcement based or otherwise. Whether we like it or not, HACCP has its own language set. This can be seen in both the core seven principles of HACCP, and in the multitude of related systems that support HACCP. Often this terminology is unnecessary, and serves to make the system less accessible than it could be. Where such words have been used in this text, this appendix offers a user-friendly definition, and, more importantly, a user's explanation of what they mean. It is not suggested these phrases need to be used all the time; the aim is to make the modern HACCP system accessible to all, removing the barriers that jargon creates.

## Good Hygiene Practice (GHP)

**Definition** *'A non-specific, non-targeted control that occurs throughout the process that can be used to address generalised hazards.'*

Sometimes referred to as generic controls.

**What does that mean?** In identifying hazards as part of principle one of HACCP it is common to find hazards that recur at just about every process step (throughout the premises). Common examples would be the chance of pest contamination, contamination from the structure of the building or areas of personal hygiene.

Control of these at one particular point is not practicable and generally they do not have clear critical limits and cannot, therefore, easily be monitored (these are obviously key principles of HACCP). If included throughout the HACCP plan they create confusion by hiding monitorable and specific critical limits.

In assessing hazards, therefore, it is possible to eliminate (or 'work out of the system') these hazards if the HACCP team is confident they are adequately addressed by current good practice. It is expected, however, that this good practice should be demonstrable to audits both by inspection and by the presence of written policy. Using the examples above, therefore, a pest control company would be employed, cleaning schedules and checklists would be in use and there would be an enforced policy on, for example, the wearing of jewellery. If this is fully complied with, this hazard can be eliminated from the HACCP approach.

In practice this means that HACCP must be built on a framework of existing, documented, good procedures. The maintenance and updating of background procedures then becomes part of the HACCP system and helps in its integration with other systems and practices. The safety of this is obviously dependent on the continued compliance with GMP documents and this should become part of regular review with the HACCP system.

## Gap Analysis

**Definition** *'A tool to enable the management and recording of system change.'*

**What does that mean?** HACCP implementation or review will require the instigation of numerous changes and improvements to the company standards or operating procedures. This change, particularly in larger organisations, can be difficult to control; improvements are not spelt out, not carried out properly, or are not completed or maintained.

To aid this, a gap analysis provides a description of required improvements that are effectively movement from point 'A' (what we have at the moment) to point 'B' (where we want to go). These are recorded and allocated a target completion date and

# HACCP 'jargon busting' glossary

process (the process steps) they occur.

The best method of a HACCP team identifying hazards is to brainstorm all hazards and then re-examine them to assess significance. A variety of tools can be used to identify hazards and these might include: the flow diagram, superimposing the flow over a plan of the premises; complaint records; monitoring records; visual inspection; or previous audit reports.

## Hazard Rating

**Definition** *'A means of assessing the significance of hazards.'*

**What does that mean?** In effect it is possible to think of some hazard at virtually any step in a process. This can result in unnecessary confusion at the stage of identifying the critical control points, and very often results in excessive CCPs. The aim of applying a rating is to remove hazards that are not significant and thus to streamline the procedure.

There are two main considerations in making such a judgement; the severity of the hazard and the risk of it being realised. A simple table can be used to make a comparative quantification of these.

## Critical Control Point (CCP)

**Definition** *'A step where control can be applied and is essential to prevent, eliminate or reduce a food safety hazard to acceptable levels.'*

**What does that mean?** Put more simply, a CCP is a point in a process (these are identified by your process flow diagram) where a hazard needs to be controlled. If it is not, the hazard will be realised and someone may become ill.

The identification of CCPs is sometimes done with the aid of a decision tree; a series of structured questions that lead to a decision on criticality.

## Critical Limit

**Definition** *' A monitorable level, which if exceeded will result in the hazard being out of control.'*

**What does that mean?** It means that we must set clear levels at critical points that can be monitored to show if the control is effective or not. If the level is exceeded then we must proceed to take corrective action. The critical limit is useless if it is something that cannot be assessed (for example, good hygiene!).

It is possible to set targets and action levels lower than the critical limit to enable action to be taken before the product becomes 'out of control'. If this is the case, the critical limit must be clearly differentiated.

## Corrective Action

**Definition** *'The action that must be taken to rectify an out-of-control situation.'*

**What does that mean?** Corrective action is fairly self-explanatory, but it can be confused. It is worth considering that corrective action where a critical limit has been exceeded is imperative and should be controlled and recorded where possible. A form such as a corrective action request (CAR) can do this.

It is also worth considering that corrective action can be aimed at two things: it can be cause specific (it addresses the reason why the product went out of its critical limit, for example, repairing a fridge); or it can be product specific (it addresses the product that has exceeded its limit, throwing away the high-risk products from the above fridge!). Most corrective action, logically, needs to address both.

## Verification

**Definition** *'A means of establishing the truth of something.'*

# HACCP 'jargon busting' glossary

**What does that mean?** You have to prove your HACCP system is telling the truth! This in effect means we must keep checking that the system is working; by comparing the document to reality, by seeking validation of the HACCP system (possibly from some external body) and by reviewing the system periodically or whenever there are changes that might affect the system.

## Impact Analysis
**Definition** *'A means of structuring human assessment of a situation and recording it.'*

**What does that mean?** Sometimes we will come across situation where we do not have clarity, for example, whether or not a product is in control. This is particularly the case with foreign bodies. In this situation, human judgement is required to make an assessment of the effect or impact.

Use of an impact assessment procedure removes some of the risk of bringing human error or bias by recording and guiding the judgements made.

## Crisis Management
**Definition** *'The action taken when an unusual crisis situation arises.'*

**What does that mean?** It means that things go wrong sometimes. Extortion, product withdrawals, food poisoning claims can happen due to events beyond our control.

A company's reaction is crucial. As far as possible a company should try and pre-empt such situations by having recorded crisis management procedures, covering actions, responsibilities, contact numbers, press releases, etc.

# References

1. Campden and Chorleywood Research Association, *HACCP: A Practical Guide* (1997) Chipping Campden

2. Chadwick House Group Ltd, *Industry Guides To Good Practice (Catering, Wholesale, Retail, Markets, Baking)* CHG Ltd, London

3. Chartered Institute of Environmental Health, *Environmental Health News* (Weekly publication) CIEH, London

4. Chartered Institute of Environmental Health, *HACCP Practitioner* (Six-yearly publication) CIEH, London

5. Chartered Institute of Environmental Health, *HACCP in Practice: Course Handbook* (1998) [Training Course, Materials and Certification] CIEH, London

6. Chartered Institute of Environmental Health, *Intermediate Certificate in Hazard Analysis* [Training Course, Materials and Certification] CIEH, London

7. Codex Alimentarius Committee on Food Hygiene, *Guidelines for the Application of the Hazard Analysis and Critical Control Point System* (1993) World Health Organization, Rome

8. Codex Alimentarius Committee on Food Hygiene, *The HACCP System and Guidelines for Its Application)* (1997) World Health Organization, Rome

9. Commission of the European Communities, *White Paper on Food Safety* COM (1999) Final

10. Commission of the European Communities, *Official Journal No L 175/1 Council Directive 93/43/EEC of the 14th June on the Hygiene of Foodstuffs* (1993) European Commission, Brussels

11. Department of Health, *Assured Safe Catering* The Stationery Office, London

12. Dillon, Mike and Griffiths, Chris, *How to Audit: Verifying Food Control Systems* (1997) Midway Technology, UK

13. HCIMA, Technical Briefing N0 5, HACCP - *The Effective Approach to Food Hygiene and Safety* HCIMA, London

14. *The Meat Products Regulations (1994) As Amended* (1994) The Stationery Office, London

15. *The Food Safety Act* (1990) The Stationery Office, London

16. *The Food Safety Act (1990) Code of Practice No 9* (1990) The Stationery Office, London

17. *The Fresh Meat (Hygiene and Inspection) Regulations (1995)* The Stationery Office, London

18. *The Wild Game Meat (Hygiene and Inspection) Regulations (1995)* The Stationery Office, London

19. *The Poultry Meat, Farmed Game and Bird Meat, and Rabbit Meat (Hygiene and Inspection) Regulations (1995)* The Stationery Office, London

# References

20. *The Food Safety (General Food Hygiene) Regulations 1995* The Stationery Office, London

21. *The Food Safety (Fishery Products and Live Shellfish) Regulations 1998* The Stationery Office, London

22. *The Dairy Products (Hygiene) Regulations 1995* The Stationery Office, London

23. *The Food Safety (General Food Hygiene) (Butchers Shop) Amendment Regulations 2000* The Stationery Office, London

24. International Standards Organisation *The ISO 9000 Series of Quality Management and Quality Assurance Standards* (2000) ISO

25. Johns, Nicholas, *Managing Food Hygiene* (1991) MacMillan, UK

26. Meat and Livestock Commission *Accelerated HACCP Training for Meat Managers* (1998) Pub MLC, UK

27. National Academy of Science, *Classification of Food Products According to Risk* National Academy Press, USA

28. National Research Council, *An Evaluation of the Role of Microbiological Criteria for Foods and Food Ingredients* (1985) National Academy Press, USA

29. Pennington Group, *Report on the Circumstances Leading to the 1996 Outbreak of Infection with E. coli O157 and the Implication for Food Safety* (1997) The Stationery Office, London

30. QSA.HACCP Software Package. QSA Ltd, Wellington House 273-275 High St, London Colney, St. Albans Herts, AL2 1ZW

31. RIPH, *Intermediate Certificate in Applied HACCP Principles* [Course and Certification], RIPH London

32. RIPH, *HACCP Principles and their Application in Food Safety Training Standard (Advanced)* (1999) RIPH, London

33. Sprenger, Richard, *Hygiene for Management (Nineth Edition 2002)* Highfield Publications, Doncaster, UK

34. Wallace, Carole and Mortimore, Sara, *A Practical Approach to HACCP (Training Program)* Aspen

35. Wallace, Carole and Mortimore, Sara, *HACCP A Practical Approach (2nd Edition)* Aspen

*Regulations are available from the Stationery Office, London.*

# Answers to revision questions

If these are being used as part of structured learning please bear in mind that discussion of the wrong answers is a valuable learning tool.

**PART ONE: PREREQUISITES**
1. b)
2. c) (because they form part of CCP monitoring)
3  d)
4  a)

**PART TWO: PRINCIPLE ONE**
1. a)
2. b)
3. c)
4. b)

**PART THREE: PRINCIPLE TWO**
1. c)
2. d)

**PART FOUR: PRINCIPLES THREE TO FIVE**
1. a)
2. c)
3. b)
4. b)
5. c)
6. d)

**PART FIVE: PRINCIPLES SIX TO SEVEN**
1. c)
2. d)
3. a)